Donated by

Warren Kump M.D.

© DEMCO, INC. 1990 PRINTED IN U.S.A.

The Life and Times of
Emil H. Grubbe

The Life and Times of Emil H. Grubbe

Paul C. Hodges, M.D.

The University of Chicago Press
CHICAGO AND LONDON

Library of Congress Catalog Card Number: 64–24977
THE UNIVERSITY OF CHICAGO PRESS, CHICAGO & LONDON
The University of Toronto Press, Toronto 5, Canada
© 1964 by The University of Chicago. All rights reserved. Published 1964.
Printed in the United States of America.
Chicago, Illinois, U.S.A.

He was a man, take him for all in all
Hamlet

Foreword

Emil Herman Grubbe was born in Chicago on January 1, 1875. For his first quarter-century, this son of Janus prospered as though the benign face of his natal god controlled his destiny, but for the ensuing decades until his death on March 26, 1960, at the age of eighty-five, frustration, marital unhappiness, disfigurement, and pain came to him in such measure that at times he may well have felt himself to be the victim of Janus's vindictive other nature.

One of Chicago's earliest X-ray workers, he, like so many other pioneers, received hopelessly heavy irradiation of hands, face, and other body parts, and undoubtedly much of the unhappiness of his later life was caused by the progressive effects of extensive X-ray damage, which required numerous excisions and amputations. In spite of increasingly frequent and extensive surgery, he continued to practice until 1948. However, by his fiftieth year family and social contacts had dwindled, and he had become almost pathologically preoccupied with the past. Grubbe was a convinced and ardent atheist; as far as he was concerned, his only immortality could be through his works.

By the time his surgical marathon began to attract the attention of writers, Dr. Grubbe had formulated a mental outline of his achievements which, with repeated retelling, hardened into a legend accepted as fact, not only by the readers of a torrent of sympathetic, nondocumented newspaper and magazine stories, but even by the subject himself. According to the legend, Dr. Grubbe had worked with X-rays well in advance of their discovery by Roentgen and was the first human being to be injured by them and the first to employ them therapeutically; he claimed to be the first in a total of eleven aspects of radiology.

Why disturb the legend? Dr. Grubbe himself has made this necessary by bequeathing the major portion of his estate to support the practice and teaching of radiation therapy at the University of Chicago and stipulating that the university prepare and publish a biography of him. Undoubtedly, he hoped such a book would defend his priority claims, but even if available evidence justified this, it would be a biography not worth reading, much less writing, if its principal aim were personal vindication. As a matter of fact, many of the claims are palpably erroneous and it is not certain that more than one can be defended to the hilt, but this is unimportant. What is important is that Emil Grubbe truly was a pioneer; that his early life spanned three or four decades of interesting and important change in medical education and practice, not only in Chicago but throughout the land; and particularly that it included the twilight years of the long-since defunct "electrotherapy" and the childhood of that lusty branch of medicine now known as radiology.

Dr. Grubbe's work as a physician started in 1898, and for all practical purposes was completed by 1918, leaving him largely an observer of the scene for the following four decades. During his active period, he employed "gas" X-ray tubes almost exclusively, and his most valid work was in the superficial therapy of skin cancer. Following 1918, shorter wave-length, heavily filtered beams, and the concept of the tissue dose became basic to radiation therapy; but he had little appreciation of these matters and to the time of his death clung to numerous fallacies, including the belief that an X-ray beam is made up of alpha, beta, and gamma rays.

It is now merely trite rather than risqué to say that a man has "guts," but no other expression describes quite so well Emil Grubbe's enthusiasm, vitality, and pugnacity. At an age when modern boys ride to and from school and social engagements in maternally chauffeured family cars, he was supporting himself, living in his own quarters, and cooking his own meals. If he lacked a high school education and chose a college which at that time smacked strongly of the diploma mill, it must be admitted that in his day such schools were the rule rather than the exception, and in the matter of his medical training it must be remembered that even fifteen years later the average medical school was a national disgrace, with Chicago, "the plague spot of the country," [1] supporting fourteen medical schools of which only three or four were respectable.

The Emil Grubbe legend is now too well established to give way to the more factual picture which follows presently, and I believe this is as he would have it. For my part, however, I prefer the factual Grubbe. I see him as a tough, shrewd, intelligent, relatively uneducated second-generation European, clawing his way up in the social and economic struggle that was being repeated thousands of times all about him in the Chicago of his youth; asking and giving no quarter, dreaming great dreams, turning some of them into hard fact and in others substituting for frustration the illusion of fact.

The University of Chicago has made available to me all of Dr. Grubbe's papers, including reprints, diplomas, and citations, disk recordings of interviews with radio commentators, and four magnetic tapes, recording some seven hours of interview by Mr. Elliott McCleary, a professional writer, who at one time contemplated a Grubbe biography of his own. These, together with Grubbe's own book, *X-Ray Treatment—Its Origin, Birth, and Early History*,[2] constitute the direct sources of this book. Most of Grubbe's notes date from the ten or twenty years before his death, and so must have come from memory or imagination. Emil himself stated that the largest part of his personal effects had been lost in a fire, and several extant papers, which he said were in a barrel rescued from the fire, do indeed bear the marks of rescue.

In addition to librarians at the University of Wisconsin and throughout the Chicago area and colleagues in history, geology, chemistry, and other departments of the University of Chicago, I am indebted to the secretaries of numerous national societies; the Honorable Paul H. Douglas, U.S. Senator from Illinois; the U.S. Passport Bureau; Mr. Howard H. Moore, legal counsel, University of Chicago; officers of Loyola, Valparaiso, and Indiana universities; numerous radiologists currently or formerly in charge of radiology services at leading Chicago hospitals and clinics; Dr. Otto Glasser of the Cleveland Clinic; members of the staff of the Smith-

---

[1] Abraham Flexner, *Medical Education in the United States* (Carnegie Foundation, 1910), p. 216.
[2] St. Paul and Minneapolis: Bruce Publishing Co., 1949.

sonian Institution and the Argonne National Laboratory; several of Dr. Grubbe's contemporaries and physicians, and particularly his faithful friend and long-time confidante, Mrs. Elisabeth Earle.

In matters not crucial to Emil's priority claims, I have accepted his statements because to have done otherwise would have required laborious consultation of contemporary public records beyond my competence and inconsistent with the importance of matters under consideration. Probably this material is not more inaccurate than most other undocumented recollections.

Where a point is important I have, however, done all in my power to check Dr. Grubbe's statements against established facts, sometimes with devastating results—but in one instance with complete vindication. Two January, 1896, letters, written by Doctors Ludlam and Halphide and now in the Smithsonian Institution, are of the greatest importance because it is they alone which bolster Dr. Grubbe's claim to having applied X-rays therapeutically in January, 1896. At the outset, I assumed that the letters were at worst frank forgeries, at best genuine but with altered dates; but I was wrong. At my urging, the Smithsonian submitted them to one of the nation's most respected crime detection laboratories, where it was established that there was no evidence of erasures; that paper, ink, style of writing, and other details were in keeping with the purported date of writing; and that the Ludlam signature appeared to have been written by the same hand that penned other unquestionably genuine Ludlam signatures I was able to submit for comparison.

If my skepticism seems excessive, let me remind the reader of Lord Raglan's book, *The Hero*,[3] in which we are told of Elizabethan and ancient Grecian forgeries so skillfully done that they deceived generations of scholars.

The chapter headings can be defended only on the score of convenience because, of course, life as it is being lived does not fit neatly into compartments. Even the story defies strict compartmentalization and repeatedly cuts back or leaps forward during the telling. The title of Chapter III, "The Controversial Years," by no means implies that previous to 1895 gaps in our knowledge of

---

[3] Lord Raglan, *The Hero: A Study in Tradition, Myth, and Drama* (New York: Vintage Books, 1956), pp. 18, 24.

the actual facts are not of basic importance and that subsequent to 1898 contemporary records become increasingly plentiful. It is rather that those three years between graduation from college and then from medical school (the period of discovery and early clinical application of X-rays) are the most crucial to the Grubbe priority claims and at the same time most lacking in documentation other than by his own statements, most of which originated many years after the event.

Contents

The Life and Times of
Emil H. Grubbe

One

ON A NEW KIND OF RAYS

The timing of events immediately related to Roentgen's discovery of X-rays is established now beyond reasonable doubt by the scholarly historical research of Otto Glasser, L. Zehnder, numerous other German writers, and the staff of the Deutsches Roentgen-Museum in Lennep. The discovery was made November 8, 1895; reprints of a now famous paper, "On a New Kind of Rays," [1] dated December 28, 1895, were mailed to selected physicists on January 1, 1896; the story broke in a Vienna newspaper January 5, 1896, and was cabled widely January 6, 1896.

It was January 9 before the story made the pages of the paper in Würzburg, where the discovery had been made, and meanwhile it had appeared in an electrical journal in New York on January 8. New York and London medical journals told of Roentgen's work January 11, but the first Chicago newspaper accounts appeared on Sunday and Monday, January 19 and 20, and the *Journal of the American Medical Association* waited until February to discuss the probable value of the new rays in medicine.

When did Grubbe first learn of the discovery? We can merely guess the exact date, but it could not have been earlier than January 6, and there is no reason to suppose it was later than January 19. The point is important in evaluating his priority claims.

In 1933, or shortly earlier, Dr. Grubbe began reading at the John Crerar Library in preparation for his paper, "Priority in the Therapeutic Use of X-rays," [2] but, unfortunately, the sources available to him at that time lacked the objectivity and validity that have

---

[1] Otto Glasser, *Dr. W. C. Roentgen* (Springfield, Ill.: Charles C. Thomas, 1958).

[2] See Appendix I.

come in later years with the release of contemporary correspondence and the records of German scientific societies and of the Prussian government. The picture was still clouded also by the dust of misinformation kicked up in the early weeks of 1896 by newspaper sensationalism and voluble statements of a welter of "experts" who, drawing deeply on their ignorance of the subject, gave forth preposterous statements, explanations, and predictions. Presumably, the accounts in Chicago's major newspapers of the period were neither better nor worse than those in other American papers, and presumably all of them were mere embellishments of a basic syndicated piece prepared in New York.

His German background saved Grubbe from difficulty with Roentgen's name, a difficulty which persists down to this day in some quarters. Röntgen (anglicized *Roentgen*) is pronounced "Rent/gen," the "g" being hard as in "get." The first cable from London had it misspelled as "Routgen."

The Inter-Ocean (one cent in Chicago, two cents elsewhere) of Sunday, January 19, carried the story on page nine in three columns, with two line drawings and the heading, "Getting the Insides: Photography through Opaque Substances." Some German-speaking member of the editorial staff had corrected the silly blunder in the spelling of Roentgen's name, but for the most part the New York story was printed verbatim, including a statement from Thomas Edison which has added nothing to his scientific stature. The X-rays, he said, were long wave-length heat rays. That explained their penetrating ability. They could be used to explore ocean depths and to locate diamonds and precious metals in the earth. Or a burglar might misuse them to determine in advance whether a particular safe contained valuables.

The *Tribune* put the story on page 38 of its Sunday, January 19, edition, using two full columns, including not only a local rework of the two illustrations used by the *Inter-Ocean*, but also a third purporting to be an X-ray picture of the entire skeleton of a male seated beside a fully clothed female who, for modesty's sake, had not been included in the X-ray beam.

The *Sunday Times-Herald* of January 19 used two columns and two figures on page 25 with still more on the following page, first to tell the story as it had come from New York and then to bring a little real sense into the account by interviews with two Chi-

cagoans. Dr. Frank Lydston found preposterous Edison's suggestions that the new rays could be used to detect pearls in oysters or
assist a burglar in weighing in advance the possible loot in a safe.
He said, quoting Carlyle, "This was mere watered moonshine."
A. J. Michelson, University of Chicago physicist and subsequently
Nobel prize winner, who had received one of the reprints mailed
from Würzburg January 1, held Roentgen and his work in the
highest regard but pointed out that investigations into the nature
and properties of the rays had barely begun and that in his opinion
it was a little too soon to evaluate their importance to medicine.
As to some of Edison's pronouncements, Michelson doubted that
the rays would be found useful in locating minerals deep in the
earth.

The Chicago Record on January 20 carried the following story
on page 6 as a paragraph in a column on "Science and Industry":

> Scientists are greatly interested in the report of experi-
> ments at Würzburg, repeated at Budapest, in which a light
> has been used which, for the purposes of photography, will
> penetrate wood, flesh, and many other organic substances.
> It is said that Professor ROUTGEN, the inventor of the new
> system, has succeeded in photographing metal weights
> which were in a closed wooden case. . . . According to ac-
> counts from Vienna, Professor ROUTGEN is using his dis-
> covery in photographing broken limbs and bullets. . . . It
> is curious that it can be done without a lens. Its use . . .
> promises a revolution in surgery and medicine.

We who work in radiology, and read and write and think about
it, are apt to picture the opening weeks of 1896 as given over to a
world-wide surge of interest in the marvelous new X-rays; but certainly news of them did not bulk large in the minds of those who
published these four Chicago newspapers. They had far more important subjects for the edification of their readers in that lusty
metropolis of more than one and one-half million souls, and for
the ordinary members of that populace X-rays were something to
read about and then forget.

Grubbe was no ordinary citizen, however, and instead of for-
getting he lived and thought X-rays from first hearing of them at
21 until his death 64 years later; but, unlike Samuel Pepys, he kept
no diary. There are several published polemics and literally hundreds of pounds of unindexed notes and clippings—part of which

he referred to as his "autobiography"—but almost without exception they were written some decades after the events to which they refer. Even in the matter of foreign travel one looks in vain for correspondence, passports, ticket stubs, and similar mementoes and finds merely clippings from travel sections of Sunday supplements printed many years later and carrying undated pencil notes.

Having been immersed in Grubbe material for many months, it is inevitable that I should have spun my own theory as to the probable course of events in Emil Grubbe's life during 1895–97, and though many segments of my web float on the air of guesswork, here and there it is firmly anchored to established fact. Presently, the biographee will be allowed to tell the story as he loved to tell it and as he probably believed it, and when both versions are before the reader he must choose for himself which yarn to accept.

Two

1875 – 95: Boyhood and Adolescence

From 1870 until her death at the age of 87 in 1934, Bertha Reetz Grubbe lived the quietly industrious life of a Chicago *Hausfrau*. Her two girls and two boys were raised simply in the district of Bridgeport, three miles southwest of what is today the center of the Loop. She sent them for christening and confirmation to the nearby Evangelical Lutheran Church and for instruction to parochial schools, and when she died, she followed her husband and her elder daughter to the family plot in Bethania Cemetery on Archer Avenue.

Bertha Reetz was born in 1847 at Stolp, Pomerania (now Polish Stupak), and presently moved 120 miles southwest to Pomeranian Stettin (now Polish Szeczin), where she became a nurse in one of the hospitals of that bustling Baltic port. There, fate in the year 1863 and in the form of the yet-to-be-discovered *B. typhosus* brought her as a patient and subsequently as a suitor 21-year-old Albert Grubbe, a sailor from a Baltic merchantman. The vessel was probably one of those that carried iron ore from Scandinavia and returned loaded with German coal; Emil liked to believe that his father had been the captain. Captain or seaman, after a lengthy recovery from typhoid fever he married his nurse, settled in the town, and sailed no more until the family exodus to the New World, in 1870, which presumably resulted from a desire to avoid service in Prussian armies girding for their war with France.

The name "Grubbe" has a strongly Danish flavor, but for several centuries Baltic cities and provinces had experienced repeated changes of political alignment, resulting in a scrambling of Danish, Swedish, Russian, and Prussian stock, so that by the mid-nineteenth century Danish names were common in maritime Prussia. Emil has left conflicting statements as to his father's national origin, but one of the few completely established points is the fact

5

that at the time of Albert's naturalization in Chicago, in 1876, he considered himself a subject of the Prussian emperor. The most repeated claim gave Torup in southern Sweden as the paternal birthplace; I suspect the idea developed when Emil found in the July, 1934, number of the *National Geographic* a beautifully illustrated article on Swedish castles. From that date he had no doubt that he was a direct descendant of Sigvard Grubbe who, in 1632, rebuilt ancient Torup castle and, in an inscription which is extant, admonished his descendants to cherish and preserve their inheritance. Emil's cherishing included correspondence with "genealogical researchers" and makers of coats of arms, and although there is no evidence that he swallowed whole the bait of alleged kinship to Baskervilles, Charlemagne, William the Conqueror, and Frederick Barbarossa, he certainly nibbled.

Life for the Grubbes, transplanted in 1870 from Germany to Chicago's West Side, was scarcely reminiscent of ancestral grandeur, but the Lutheran Church provided a natural rallying point, and Albert found a job in the nearby steel mills. At that time the Bridgeport mills at Archer and Ashland received their ore from vessels that threaded their way through dense river traffic, past numerous swing bridges, for the five-mile trip up from Lake Michigan; it was ten years before the mills would be relocated at their present site in South Chicago.

On two days in October, 1871, the great Chicago fire wiped out the heart of the city, taking 250 lives and destroying property worth $168,000,000, at that time an almost incomprehensible sum. The conflagration stopped short of Bridgeport, but the possibility of its spreading to include their home must have been a terrifying experience to the new arrivals from Germany. If in later years they related the story to son Emil, however, it did not impress him enough to cause him to include in his scrambled pencil jottings mention of this tragic chapter in the city's history, a scant four years before his own birth. Actually, the need for steel for rebuilding the city probably helped the immigrant Grubbes, because the Bridgeport mills remained open during the ensuing five-year national depression.

Presently, Grubbe babies began to arrive at short intervals, Emil in 1875, Hulda in 1877, Otto in 1880, and Minnie in 1883, and the wages of a single steel-mill worker were stretched very thin indeed. Whether, as was common for the period, the girls took service as domestics as soon as they were old enough to work I do not know; but Emil tells us that by the time he was thirteen he had become a wage earner.

The brief years between Emil's infancy and his attainment of man's estate at the ripe age of 13 were not devoid of pleasure, however. From his notes we know that at the age of seven he was taken to McVickers' theatre to see Mr. Edison's incandescent lamps, which in the following quarter-century were to supplant first kerosene lamps and then even gas for domestic lighting. When he was twelve, the notes tell us, there was a memorable fishing expedition to the foot of Harrison Street. The take was a three-foot eel so heavy that the aid of a friend was required to get the trophy onto the State Street cable car (over the protests of the conductor) and thence by connecting horse car to Bridgeport and home. There two families previously unacquainted with eel ate it for two days and liked it.

Most important of all to the boy was a trip to Lemont, eighteen miles away along the old Illinois-Michigan canal, as a guest on the horsedrawn scow of a neighbor, Captain Martin. The trip took four days, including a two-day stopover at Lemont. This first real journey developed in Emil a love of adventure which he never outgrew. A decade or so later, the new sanitary canal was built, reversing the flow of the Chicago River and diverting the city's raw sewage from Lake Michigan to the Illinois River. It supplied a broader and deeper commercial waterway to LaSalle and left the old canal the sole function of rewarding deserving politicians with sinecures which in the year 1901 cost the taxpayers $100,000 against toll charges totaling a mere $8,000.

Emil's first job lasted for one week; he washed windows, showcases, and bottles in a drugstore. He then moved on to more lucrative and congenial employment as cash boy, stock boy, and eventually office boy at Marshall Field's retail store at State and Madison streets. The pay was good—two dollars a week; the hours reasonable—ten hours a day, 7:30 A.M. to 5:30 P.M., with one-half hour off for lunch; and so he stayed for two years, 1888 to 1890.

Here were surroundings, personages, and occasional social contacts exactly suited to his tastes. Let others complain that Marshall Field at the age of 51 was cold and unapproachable; to Emil he

7

was a romantic figure, tall, slender, slightly bowlegged, pink-cheeked, and always impeccable in raiment and bearing. From his home at 1919 Prairie Avenue this greatly admired employer was driven daily in his carriage down Michigan Avenue to Twelfth Street, where it was his habit to leave the vehicle and complete on foot the journey to his wholesale store at Fifth Avenue and Adams Street. Later in the day, when he had to traverse the four and one-quarter miles between his wholesale and retail establishments, Field usually accomplished this too on foot, because he considered walking conducive to good health.

Emil himself, of course, used public transportation. Five years after his birth at West 31st Street, near Racine, the family had moved to 2836 Church Court, near Archer Avenue. Horse cars and connecting cable cars provided convenient, inexpensive transportation over the three and one-half miles from the boyhood home to Marshall Field and Company. This included an unusual "piggy-back" arrangement; the horse-car carried him northeast on Archer to State Street, at which point the horses were unhitched and the car was atttached to the rear of a train of cable cars for completion of the journey north on State Street to the corner of Madison.

The diligence of the new boy was rewarded presently by advancement in responsibility and wages. As a bonus, he had the opportunity to rub shoulders with men he considered important, many of whom did in fact eventually attain distinction in merchandising in Chicago, elsewhere in America, and abroad. Emil records that he relished the opportunity to mix with Chicago society at the marriage of Harry Selfridge and Rosalie Buckingham at Central Music Hall at the corner of State and Randolph streets.

By the spring of 1890, Emil had decided to become a physician and to prepare for medical school by entering Northern Indiana Normal School at Valparaiso; accordingly, he gave a month's notice of his intention to resign. Shortly thereafter, as he was leaving the wholesale building where his duties occasionally took him, his hero, Marshall Field, engaged him in conversation. Field encouraged Emil in his plans and offered him the temporary post of office boy in his own office during the two weeks' vacation of the regular incumbent, James Simpson. Emil accepted the offer, and the closing weeks of his connection with the company were memorable because of conversations with his employer in which Field encouraged him in his plans and expressed envy that Emil would be getting a college education, which Field himself had not.

It was called college, but high school would have been a more appropriate term. If he had possessed a high-school diploma, or even that nebulous quantity its "equivalent," Emil would have been eligible at almost any of Chicago's numerous schools of medicine, but a ten-hour work day had left little time for the YMCA night-school courses which constituted Emil's only formal instruction from the time he left the parochial and public grammar schools to the time he enrolled at Valparaiso.

Among Emil's few reminiscences of life at home was that of the occasional visits, in his boyhood, of an uncle who was not overly welcomed by the elder Grubbes. To his young nephew, however, he provided another window on the great, exciting outside world. Emil credits this uncle with his own interest in stamp collecting, and certain notes lead me to suspect that he may have been responsible in addition for his nephew's free-and-easy attitude toward facts, an attitude which has multiplied the problems involved in this biography. It is not recorded that the uncle was named Munchausen, but Raspe's baron would have found in him a kindred spirit.

In later years, Emil recollected vividly the teeming streets, rivers, markets, and bridges of his native metropolis. He also recorded that frequently the necessity for close observation of some particularly fascinating phenomenon on the Rush Street bridge caused him to be late for his violin lesson at the home of Mr. Edgar Pope, on Illinois Street.

It was difference of opinion as to the relative merits of professional music and medicine as careers which led eventually to a rupture in relations between Emil and his father. To Albert Grubbe, violin playing was a dignified and lucrative profession. To Emil it was "fiddle-playing." His father, however, insisted that lessons begin even before the boy was big enough to hold the instrument up to his chin properly. When Emil had made up his own mind on the subject of his future, he was convinced that he could expect no financial help from his father during college and medical school, and he decided to support himself. He was confirmed in this plan by the Grubbe family physician, Dr. E. A. Sachtleben, who knew the president of Northern Indiana Normal

9

School at Valparaiso. Dr. Sachtleben had been the first to tell Emil of the school's advantages to those of sharply limited financial means, and he wrote to his friend, the president, on Emil's behalf.

Thus, in the summer of 1890, fifteen years after his birth in Bridgeport, Emil left the parental nest to return only years later as a successful, self-made professional man, willing to forgive the father who in turn was only too happy to admit the error of his own judgment.

Present-day Valparaiso University, located in the little Indiana city of the same name, bears slight physical or academic resemblance to the institution to which Emil Grubbe was preparing to go in the spring of 1890. Fortunately for this biography, the custodian of the earlier school's records kindly has looked into them for me.

Established on a financial shoestring in 1873, its state charter named it the Valparaiso College and Northern Indiana Normal School; actually, it went by many names. In the year 1895 its diplomas read, "Northern Indiana Normal School, Valparaiso, Indiana"; in 1890 Dr. Sachtleben, discussing it with Emil, had called it Valparaiso University; in some of its advertising it called itself Valparaiso College; and in 1907 it formally adopted the designation Valparaiso University.

Although it was prosperous at first in spite of unbelievably small charges for board, room, and tuition, World War I brought evil days to the school. After several checkered years it was purchased in 1925 by a Lutheran group who have given it financial stability and greatly enhanced academic standing.

It would be helpful to know whether Emil continued without interruption (except for summer vacation) from his entrance in the spring of 1890 until his two degrees were granted, on August 15, 1895; or whether instead he attended intermittently with breaks for work, in Chicago and elsewhere, and travel; but the record is silent or confused on these and many other points. A reasonable guess is that with Chicago as a base he spent the summers of 1891–94 replenishing his financial resources, which could not have been large since they were merely what he had been able to save in some hundred weeks at Field's at an average salary of at most a few dollars—plus savings, if any, from his school-term job as night watchman at Valparaiso. Helpful too would be an explanation of why he took five years to complete work which with some application many students completed in three. Since there is ample evidence that he was diligent and of better than average intelligence, it seems to me that there can be only two answers, and of the two I strongly favor one. I find it unlikely that, although he entered in 1890 and left in 1895, he may have dropped out for two years or more through financial necessity. It is much more probable that for two years or more he worked at high school courses in Valparaiso.

My guess gains some support from three handwritten manuscripts found among his papers, dated September 2, 1892; November 6, 1892; and January 12, 1893, and titled, respectively, "The American Revolution," "Autobiography of an Old Shoe," and "Alfred the Great." In conception and syntax, these essays are more appropriate to an eighth-grader striving for freshman high school status than to a university student entered on his third collegiate year.

As a salaried night watchman Emil was required to make two complete tours of the campus each night, carrying a lighted kerosene lantern, and then promptly at 6:00 A.M. to ring the college bell, which served as an alarm clock not only for students and faculty but for townspeople as well. This employment, he says, paid all of his expenses including tuition, room, and board, and he milked from it as well what he considered to be a considerable knowledge of astronomy. As he tells the story,

> I took up the study of astronomy but in a more practical way than most students of this subject did. One of the professors had a telescope built on a hilltop he owned which was on my nightly watch route. I had a key to the telescope room on the hill and went in to view the heavens through the telescope several times each night. Needless to say, I got much practical knowledge of the universe; in fact, I got so much information that I could instruct the professor, and he considered me a valuable assistant.

By the summer of 1895, his Valparaiso experience was over. Years later, Emil had the following things to say about it:

> When I was a student at Valparaiso University in the early nineties of the last century, it was a free institution.

11

That is, it did not belong to a religious organization. Later, I became a teacher in the Chicago College of Medicine and Surgery which was the medical Department of Valparaiso University. In 1920 the Lutheran Church took over the Valparaiso city part of the University, and the Loyola University of Chicago took over the medical department. I resigned then.

I took the teachers' course, the scientific course, the pharmacy course, and the classic course.

I entered Valparaiso University in the Spring of 1890. I received Teachers' Degree in 1892, Pharmacy Degree in 1893, Scientific Degree in 1894, Classic Degree in 1895. Also in 1910 I received the Honorary Degree of LL.D.

In 1959, in a tape-recorded interview with Elliott McCleary, Emil said, in answer to the latter's questioning about college degrees:

> Well, I was a teacher in medical school and assayer for the banks. They would put in the paper, "Our assayer has found such and such things at such and such places." A classmate of mine sent this information to the President of Valparaiso. I was giving them a lot of publicity, so they gave me an honorary Ph.D. degree.

In material which he submitted to various biographical reference books on various occasions, and which appeared in, among others, *Who's Who in America*, Vol. III, he listed this highly questionable Ph.D., sometimes as having been awarded in 1895, and at other times as an honorary degree which he received in 1910. Actually, the present-day officers of Valparaiso University and Loyola Medical College find that records of their institutions contain no mention of such a degree on any date to anyone named Grubbe. Even more convincing is the fact that among Emil's carefully preserved papers, including much trash, no Ph.D. diploma was found. The actual diplomas are four in number, as follows: Graduate in Pharmacy (Ph.G.), Northern Indiana Normal School, August 15, 1895. Bachelor of Science (B.Sc.), same institution and same date. Doctor of Medicine and Surgery (M.D.), Hahnemann Medical College and Hospital of Chicago, March 24, 1898. "Certificate" from the Illinois X-ray and Electro-Therapeutic Laboratory of Chicago, January 12, 1903.

I am convinced that, if Emil had in fact ever received other diplomas, they too would have been preserved in the original and with photographic reproductions as well.

This seems an appropriate place to mention the philosophic quagmire in which medicine found itself in the period under consideration. Existing beside and in competition to the mainstream of "regular" medicine were several branches, the largest and most influential of which were "eclectic medicine" and homeopathy. The eclectics flourished very briefly; it was their ingenious notion that similarities of botanical form underlay the effectiveness of drugs against disease. Thus, if a plant resembled the form of the human liver, a drug from it must necessarily be a specific for liver disorders.

Homeopathy originated in Germany in the late eighteenth century and enjoyed considerable popularity for a hundred years, particularly in the United States. The tenets of the system, preposterous today but no more so than much of even the "regular" medical theorizing of the eighteenth and early nineteenth centuries, were conceived and enunciated in 1796 by a 41-year-old German physician, Christian Samuel Hahnemann. One of several children of a china painter in the famous Meissen porcelain factories, young Hahnemann's early education was sketchy, but he showed unusual ability as a linguist. Supported by work as a translator and librarian, he was able to attend the universities at Leipzig, Vienna, and eventually Erlangen. Seventeen years after receiving his M.D. degree from Erlangen, Hahnemann had given up trying to support his family by practicing the conventional medicine he had come to detest.

The conventional practice of medicine in Hahnemann's day smacked more of witchcraft than of science and was influenced very little by the great discoveries from the universities of Italy, France, Great Britain, and, more recently, Germany. Most patients and many physicians looked on disease as a visitation of demons and on medicaments as magic potions to exorcise them. The more serious the disease, the more strenuous must be the countermeasures; by the close of the eighteenth century these countermeasures had become so drastic that patients feared the doctor's doses of calomel, his copious, irritating, and oft-repeated enemas, and particularly his opening of their veins to relieve them of supposedly excessive blood almost more than they dreaded disease.

Over the years, many a small voice had been raised in favor of cleanliness attending childbirth and in surgery; against filth and poor housing, as favoring contagion; against handling the insane as though they were criminals or even animals; and against excessive medication and blood-letting. As a physician, Hahnemann knew the conventional measures of the period, but as a reader and translator of scientific works he knew of these other opinions as well. He was also deeply religious, and something of a mystic; with all these factors as background, he reached the conclusion that an all-powerful deity would not have afflicted mankind with disease unless, at the same time, he provided some means for its alleviation.

Hahnemann sought clues to divine intentions relative to medication by means of introspection. The answer came to him, however, as he was translating an English textbook on materia medica. Cullen, the English author, discussed among other remedies the use of chinchona in the treatment of malaria or "swamp fever," as it was known. In a flash, Hahnemann believed he remembered that when he himself had taken chinchona (the bark of a South American tree from which quinine later was isolated), it had caused him to develop fever. He had discovered, he said, the great basic law of nature, the law of similars. Diseases should be treated with drugs which produced in healthy persons symptoms similar to those of the disease being treated. Like should cure like. "*Similia similibus curantur*"; that was to be his shibboleth, and his method would be termed "homeopathy." Furthermore, since "regular" medicine treated (so it seemed to him) with opposites rather than with similars, Hahnemann coined for it the term "allopathy."

Presently, Hahnemann added two more concepts: that the therapeutic effect of a drug was enhanced by its dilution; and that most chronic disease was caused by the burrowing inward of the itch mite, which causes the skin disease known as scabies. Few of his disciples were willing to go along with number three, and many balked at number two, particularly as practiced by the master himself, with prescriptions, laboriously compounded and recompounded, containing mere fractions of billionths of a drop of the original substance.

Hahnemann lived on for almost a half-century after his first pronouncement, and for all that time and long afterward homeopathy was assailed and derided by the parent "regular" medicine. It is only fair to point out, however, that the vituperation was not unilateral; it was, in fact, initiated by Hahnemann himself, in the public press and in medical publications.

Hahnemann raged as strongly against "half homeopaths," who accepted his cult only in part, as he did against the regular physicians whom he had labeled allopaths. Not only that; he required of the faithful that they accept without question the modifications which he himself made from time to time in the "party line," and dismissed in disgrace any disciples (among them a son-in-law) who failed to do so.

As the scientific method began to revolutionize regular medicine, it left no place there for preconceived theories or beliefs about the nature of therapy or disease. Theories were useful merely as starting points for investigation, and such basic concepts as "treat with like," or "treat with unlike," disappeared. The fact that *similia similibus curantur* remained a bedrock concept for homeopathy marks its practitioners as cultists or sectarians.

One hundred twenty years after his death, Hahnemann's lasting contribution to medicine seems clear enough. His was the voice that triggered a popular revolt, long brewing, against excessive medication. That the system he offered in its place was absurd was inevitable, in view of the limited perspective of his day; but mere opposition to the old would almost certainly have failed, had it not been accompanied by the offer of something new. Latter-day apologists have stressed the fact that Hahnemann's infinitesimal doses amounted to complete withdrawal of medication, thus enabling nature to effect an unimpeded cure. There is much truth in this assertion; but it is unquestionable that the fact was *not* recognized by Hahnemann himself and was a mere accidental by-product of his dogma.

Of the 150 medical schools in the United States that were listed in the Flexner Report of 1910, 15 were homeopathic. The first such school to be established in the United States was the Homeopathic Medical College of Philadelphia, founded in 1848. It came into being in response to a decision by the nation's "regular" medical schools that they would cease to recognize apprenticeship to a homeopathic physician as fulfilling the requirements for entrance. Like others that followed, including Hahnemann Medical College in Chicago, the Philadelphia school provided instruction in all the subjects covered by the "regular" schools and in addition taught the homeopathic pharmacopeia. Its graduates received not only an M.D. degree but also the degree of Doctor of Homeopathy. Although the D.H. was awarded as late as 1950, since 1927 there has been little of homeopathy about the school.

In the years before and after the Civil War, homeopathy gained many adherents in the United States, some of whom were prominent and influential. Some historians have considered this the natural result of heavy emigration from Germany, the new arrivals bringing revolt against established medicine along with religious and political revolt. Another factor may have been the prevailing American passion for personal "liberty"; regular medicine, in opposing homeopathy, might be said to be curtailing the individual's freedom to select for himself the type of medical care he preferred. Under political pressure, the universities of Michigan, Iowa, Ohio, and Minnesota were forced to add homeopathic schools to their "regular" medical schools, but all students were required to take identical work in the first two years, and as soon as it became possible to require identical admission standards for all entrants, the homeopathic branches withered and died.

Emil Grubbe's alma mater, Hahnemann Medical College of Chicago, existed for 63 years, opening in 1859 and closing in 1922. In 1964, the year of writing, homeopathy is no longer taught in the United States. A single homeopathic pharmacy in Chicago does principally a mail-order business with the dwindling number of physicians, largely in the South, who still prescribe the infinitely diluted remedies of Christian Samuel Hahnemann.

Three

1895 – 98: THE CONTROVERSIAL YEARS

> *Fabulous tales ought to be suited to the reader's under-*
> *standing, being so contrived that all impossibilities ceasing,*
> *all great accidents appearing feasible, and the mind wholly*
> *hanging in suspense, they may at once surprise, astonish,*
> *please, and divert: so that pleasure and admiration may go*
> *hand in hand.*—CERVANTES.

If Emil Grubbe had lived under the restraining influence of an intrepid wife or properly skeptical children, or if he had been a voracious and catholic reader, the work of his biographer might have been easier. But since he was childless and long divorced, there were none to meet Grubbe pronouncements with the challenges they would have encountered in normal home surroundings. The thousand voices from the past on library shelves waited in vain for an opportunity to teach him the unreliability of human memory unbolstered by documents and the pitfalls inherent in documents themselves. None of us would be blameless if it were a character defect to be unable to recall accurately facts and dates about our affairs, ourselves, and our dear ones, but few are guilty of the degree of glibness with which Emil answered questions posed by others and spoke for himself. This glibness led him to give several different birth and death dates for his parents and siblings and conflicting information as to his father's national origin, and to make statements, sometimes merely confused but often blatantly untrue, relative to his academic degrees and to events leading up to his early work with X-rays.

I had intended to tell his own story of these events by stringing together actual quotations from such sources as his book, penciled notes, and tape recordings of interviews, but the result of this method is both tiresome to read and unjust to the biographee. Instead, I have paraphrased statements from his book, publications, and the McCleary interview, weeding, abbreviating, rearranging, and boiling down thousands of words into a few hundred. Cervantes' postulates for writing a fabulous tale certainly have been fulfilled here. Alleged facts fit neatly together in a most convincing fashion; but, sparked by an almost culpable skepticism, I have numbered thirteen points, susceptible of objective proof, on which the narrative rests, followed by the source of each assertion.

The summer vacations during his college years Emil worked as an assayer and metallurgist, first in the laboratory of Arthur Small at Clark Street south of Harrison, then, after Small's death in 1895, as owner of the business, which he says he bought from the estate for $550. In the summer of 1895, he worked in a small room facing the alley in the rear of Grant's stationery store at 12 Pacific Avenue (now LaSalle Street) and in the basement had a room for refining metals. The building, known as the Traders' Building, housed numerous gold miners' agents. After ore samples had served their promotional purposes, these agents or the banks with whom they dealt had no further use for the ore and were glad to turn it over to a boy Emil employed to collect it and bring it to his basement room, where he smelted it down and recovered the precious metals it contained.

Working for Mr. Small, and later for himself, he says he traveled widely during the summer months to Mexico, Canada, British Columbia, and particularly to the western part of the United States, collecting samples of gold ore for analysis. *Emil contends that at that time there were no banks west of Chicago interested in lending money for the development of gold mines* (1) *and that he was the only assayer in Chicago and therefore very busy.* (2) These two contentions are from the McCleary interview.

(1) Research has shown that Chicago banks certainly were active in financing mining during the period under question, but they faced stiff competition from California banks.

(2) The *Lakeside Directories* of Chicago for 1895 and the years shortly before and after that date list approximately a dozen assayers and mining chemists in Chicago, none of them named Small or Grubbe.

In the summer of 1895, while on a trip to Cripple Creek, Colorado, on behalf of the First National Bank of Chicago, Emil alleges he discovered the first gold ore to be taken at that site. Later, on business for the First National and also the Illinois Bank of Chicago, he says he visited Gunnison, Colorado, and *in July or August, 1895, while at a placer mine in the Snake River in Idaho, recognized something which the miners had overlooked—namely, that the sand in the river bottom contained platinum.* (3)

This assertion originates in the copious notes I have designated Emil's autobiography.

(3) From the U.S. Geological Survey of mineral resources of the United States for 1913, and from "The Minerals of Idaho," Bulletin 131, 1926, pages 75–76, I have learned that except in the (unverified) case of Minidoka County, only the merest traces of platinum have been found in the state of Idaho. In the case of Minidoka County, black sands from the Snake River, first reported as showing 0.018 ounces per ton, were found on investigation to be not samples of the natural sand but gravels concentrated several thousands of times. Workers at the large placer mines were well aware that at "clean-up time," when they thinned the gold amalgam with fresh mercury to free it of foreign material, gray specks of platinum always floated to the top. In the course of several years, one engineer had collected a quarter-ounce of such platinum sand, which he exhibited as a curiosity. The much more plentiful metals such as gold, which were the objectives of the mining, ran only one-quarter to one per cent of the gravel handled.

In the year 1913 the total platinum production in all the large gold mines in California and Oregon amounted to only 482.87 ounces, valued at $18,477. The best of the Russian mines run 0.05 ounces per ton.

Emil was able to make this "discovery," he says, because he had seen such platinum-bearing sand in the laboratory at Valparaiso. Later, when the sand had been shipped to Chicago, he maintains he was able to confirm his suspicion in his own laboratory after he had designed an electric furnace to do the smelting.

Emil's banker employers were not interested in platinum, he says. All they wanted was gold, and this in spite of the fact that, according to Emil, *the market value of platinum at that time was $136* an ounce whereas that of gold was only $32.00 an ounce. (4) (Mc-Cleary interview.)

(4) For the ten-year period 1903–13, the total U.S. production of platinum rose from a value of $2,080 for 110 ounces in 1903 (less than $19.00 an ounce) to $46,530 for 1,034 ounces in 1913 (slightly less than $50.00 an ounce), and the 1903 price constituted "a marked rise" since the year 1898. Presumably, therefore, if Emil Grubbe had any platinum at all in the year 1895, it consisted of a few grains obtained from placer miners as a curiosity, and its value was nearer $19.00 an ounce than the alleged $136.

Accordingly, in the fall of 1895 he says he formed the Moraine Mining and Manufacturing Company to develop the platinum project. (5) Emil says that in Chicago he paid $150 for a second-hand horse-drawn steam fire engine, shipped it to Idaho, and with it pumped up sand and water from the river bottom. This mixture, he says, he strained through wire window screens, and during the month of September pumped up and shipped to Chicago sand which yielded $25,000 worth of pure platinum. (6) This platinum was put into a safety deposit box which Emil says he rented at the First National Bank of Chicago. (7) Some months later, after burning his hands with X-rays, Emil says he gave up this phase of his work, sold out his mining interest to others, and had no knowledge of what they did with the property. These three claims are all made in the McCleary interview.

(5) The office of the Secretary of State in Springfield, Illinois, informs me that the Moraine Mining Company was incorporated in 1902 and dissolved in 1926. Emil's files contain a receipt for $100 dated July 9, 1902, for money paid to a Dr. J. E. Gilman in connection with legal action against the Midvale Mining Company of Idaho, at a time when Emil said he had given up all interest in mining.

(6) Water pumps were used by placer miners to wash gravel into various types of concentrating devices, but the pumps handled only water and would have failed within minutes if close-fitting pistons and cylinders had been subjected to tons or even ounces of sand, to say nothing of coarse gravel. Among the myriad newspaper clippings in his personal papers, most of them dating only from the decade or so before his death, Emil has saved one from

an advertisement of AC Fuel Pumps showing a horse-drawn, smoke-belching fire engine. The date of the clipping probably is August, 1952, and it carries Emil's penciled notation: "the kind I bought secondhand and used to pump platinum-bearing sand out of the Snake River in Idaho (1895)."

(7) Friends on the staff of the First National Bank of Chicago have gone to the trouble of opening warehouses containing old records, only to find that no one named Grubbe rented a safety deposit box in 1895 or earlier or for many years thereafter.

In those days platinum had not yet come into fashion for jewelry, and one of its main uses was in the electrical industry, where among other applications it was used to carry electrical circuits through the walls of glass containers such as incandescent lamp bulbs. Seeking an outlet for his fortune in platinum, Emil says he decided to undertake the manufacture of electric light bulbs and accordingly engaged a newly arrived German glass blower named Albert Schmidt, who happened to come to his door seeking work.

Schmidt is described as knowing how to build and operate exhaust pumps, and soon, according to Emil, the two were producing not only electric light bulbs but also Geissler tubes and a little mica-vane radiometer tube which had been invented by Sir William Crookes. Schmidt is supposed to have brought with him several German books and journals and, following his advice, Emil now subscribed to *Annalen der Physik und Chemie*, where in the September number he says he read of Lenard's experiments with cathode rays and proceeded to repeat them. Most of their time had to be spent making electric light bulbs, but he says that in the evening he and Schmidt worked for the fun of it with other types of tubes, including some of the type made by Crookes long after his invention of the radiometer. When certain problems were encountered, *Emil claims he wrote to Crookes, who not only answered but also presented him with copies of several of his books.* (8) This assertion is in the autobiography.

(8) If Sir William Crookes did indeed send him books in 1895, or at any time before or after that date, Grubbe did not consider them of sufficient value to preserve. They are not among the papers turned over to his biographer nor are they among the 54 volumes

he presented to the Crerar Library or the two or three received by the University of Chicago. (The "thousand" about which so much was written in the popular press have eluded my most careful search.)

Emil says that on November 6, 1895, Professor W. C. Roentgen of Würzburg, Germany, disclosed in writing to the Physical Institute of his University the fact that on the previous day he had discovered a new form of radiation which he named X-rays. Emil believed that on November 8 Roentgen's report on this was published, that one week later, the discovery was written up in a Würzburg newspaper, (9) and that recognizing the medical implications of his work, Roentgen reported it on December 28, 1895, to the local physical-medical society. (Autobiography.)

(9) As was explained in chapter I, the myth of the November, 1895, disclosure by Roentgen, once widely believed, has been disproved. Grubbe could not have known of Roentgen's work earlier than January 6, 1896, and he may not have learned of it until a week later than that.

At the time of the alleged November announcement, Emil had become a medical student at Hahnemann Medical College and in addition had been appointed to teach physics and chemistry at that institution.

In connection with the chemistry teaching, he says it was necessary for him to write and copyright a textbook on chemistry because of the rapidity with which that subject was developing. *Emil says that in 1894, the last of his student years at Valparaiso, so little was known of the nature of that simple substance, water, that its chemical formula was given as HO, but that by the following year expanding theory had established the correct formula to be the now familiar H_2O. (10)*

(10) If Emil's chemistry teachers at Northern Indiana Normal School in the year 1894 still believed that the proper formula for water was HO, they must have stopped their scientific reading with books printed about 1861. At least as early as 1869, Roscoe's *Elementary Chemistry* ([New York: William Wood and Co.] p. 28) used the symbol H_2O.

* * *

Emil claims that because he was a chemist and a physicist as well as a manufacturer of vacuum tubes, the announcement of Roentgen's discovery found him probably the only person in the United States equipped immediately to duplicate the experiments which led to the discovery. As a matter of fact, he says that like all other workers with vacuum discharge tubes, he had already been working with X-rays without realizing the fact.

According to the story, Schmidt and Emil now redoubled their efforts. *They recalled that in 1894, Herbert Jackson in England had shown that a convex cathode would focus the cathode rays, and as soon as they used his convex cathode in their homemade tubes the X-ray output improved strikingly.* (11) In order to determine X-ray output while the tubes were still on the pump, and thus know when a sufficient vacuum had been obtained, *Emil claims he invented what has come to be known as the fluoroscope,* (12) using for this purpose platinum-barium-cyanide which he prepared from platinum he had personally discovered, mined, and smelted. Both assertions appear in the autobiography. He commonly held his left hand close to the tube that was being exhausted, watching the image of the hand on the fluoroscopic screen until the radiation became sufficiently "hard" to cause the shadows of the soft tissue to disappear and only those of the bones remain.

(11) While it is true that Herbert Jackson and Crookes had used concave negative electrodes in cathode-ray tubes earlier than 1895, it was not until March 13, 1896, that Jackson himself realized the advisability of employing such cathodes in X-ray tubes, did so, and published the fact.

(12) Grubbe is not alone in claiming fatherhood of the fluoroscope. Edison made a similar claim, and there were several others. Actually, Roentgen himself did the work early in his experiments but did not bother to press his priority or dispute the claims of others.

Emil says that he and Schmidt made such tubes only for their own use and did not manufacture them commercially, but that they were deeply interested in the new form of radiation, and for many hours a day for many days in succession, in the fall and early winter of 1895 and in January, 1896, exposed Emil's body to X-rays.

23

Toward the end of January, 1896, Emil noticed severe itching on the back of the left hand followed shortly by swelling, inflammation, pain, blistering, loss of hair (epilation), and eventually breaking down of the skin (desquamation). That was the state of affairs, he says, when on January 27, 1896, he attended a faculty meeting of the medical college where he was both student and teacher. Several of his physician colleagues and teachers, noticing that his hand was bandaged, inquired about it and when the bandage had been removed offered therapeutic suggestions. One of the group, Dr. J. E. Gilman, instead of advising as to treatment expressed the belief that if X-rays could be so damaging to normal tissues they might be effective against disease tissues such as neoplasm. This idea impressed the other physicians who were present and two of them offered to send Emil cancer patients if he cared to make a therapeutic trial. In this manner, the ground was laid for the birth of radiation therapy.

At 10:00 A.M., on Wednesday, January 29, 1896, Mrs. Rose Lee, a patient of Dr. R. Ludlam, came to Emil's little place at 12 Pacific Avenue and he administered the first of eighteen treatments to a carcinoma of her left breast which had recurred after a first and then a second operation. The treatments reduced her pain, but she died about a month after the first visit.

Early on the next day (Thursday, January 30, 1896) his second patient arrived with a note from Dr. A. C. Halphide, Emil's professor of pathology. Dr. Halphide requested that Emil administer X-rays to twelve-year-old lesions of lupus vulgaris on the right cheek and jaw of his eighty-year-old patient, Mr. A. Carr. As in the case of Mrs. Lee, he used a treatment time of one hour and Mr. Carr experienced relief of pain following each treatment, but after twenty-one treatments had been given he was killed in a fall on the street.

Emil points out that at the time these two pioneering events occurred, he had barely started the study of medicine, knew little of the means by which one publishes his work, and claims he probably would not have been able to get a medical journal to accept a paper even if he had written one. Later, after he had graduated and become an accepted physician, many others had published papers on X-ray treatment, some unaware of Emil's pioneer work, and others choosing deliberately to ignore it.

His work did not go unnoticed in Chicago, however. More and more patients were referred to his little dusty, fume-filled metallurgy laboratory, behind Grant's stationery store, ill-suited as it was to clinical work; and his teachers indicated they would send still more if the facilities could be improved. Accordingly, in February, 1896, Emil gave up all other forms of work (except teaching and studying at Hahnemann) and moved from 12 Pacific Avenue to 2614 Cottage Grove Avenue, where a second-floor laboratory was devoted exclusively to X-ray work. This was, he believed, the world's first radiation therapy laboratory. The work in the new location drew fire from physicians who were ignorant of X-rays and suspicious of them, and Emil was called a faker and a quack, a charge to which he was particularly vulnerable because he had not yet received a medical degree.

By the spring of 1898 there had been added to his B.S. and Pharmacy degrees the M.D. degree, which made him at last a full-fledged doctor and opened a new era in his life. *He claimed that later he received a Ph.D., LL.D., and many honorary degrees.* (13) This last claim appears in all three direct sources.

(13) Among Emil's carefully preserved diplomas, citations, membership certificates, etc., there is no record of degrees beyond one B.S. and one Ph.G. (Graduate in Pharmacy) from Valparaiso and one M.D. from Hahnemann. I have searched for others and have written to the officials of the institutions from which he says others were obtained, but to not avail.

There is no information about the physical findings, technique of therapy, or clinical results in other patients treated either in the little room on Pacific Avenue or, after February, 1896, at 2614 Cottage Grove. Emil says merely, "Here I continued to make use of X-rays for treatment purposes for several years. Most of the . . . patients referred to me . . . were . . . moribund and . . . many . . . died soon after I began to make X-ray applications. After . . . a short period . . . patients exhibiting more favorable . . . conditions arrived for treatment [and] . . . in some . . . the results . . . were so striking as to create quite a sensation.

"Soon my work increased to such an extent that I had to have assistants to help me give the treatments. Patients came not only from all parts of the city but also from out of the city and even from distant places." Deeper insight into Emil's methods and results may be gained from material in Appendix I.

The quarters at 2614 Cottage Grove remained in use for some years after graduation with other offices in the Loop, and even the 12 Pacific Avenue place was maintained for a time for such assaying and metal recovery jobs as came his way. At first glance, the Hahnemann time schedule for second-year students seems to preclude even the teaching of chemistry to say nothing of other jobs, because students had assigned work from 9:30 A.M. to 4:30 P.M. six days a week, but presumably catalogue window-dressing and student adeptness at cutting classes were as commonplace in 1895 as they are today. In any event, Emil found time not only for an increasingly large radiology practice on Cottage Grove Avenue, but for other activities as well, including service for a year as executor of the estate of his late friend, A. B. Griswold, and the management of Griswold's newspaper delivery service. No doubt the income was welcome, but years later the most highly prized feature of the newspaper work was seen to have been the opportunity of meeting such customers as Mr. Higginbothem, the President of the Columbian Exposition, the Reverend Gunsaulus, Philip Armour, Dr. John B. Murphy, Dr. Arthur Dean Bevan, and many other prominent south siders.

Like a needle in a haystack, a sound orange floating in a welter of harbor trash, or genuine cry of "Wolf!," truth may escape detection when it is surrounded by simulated truth. At first I doubted everything, even the existence of those two patients on January 29 and 30, 1896. This latter doubt, at least, has been dispelled, but the blame for my skepticism rests on Emil Grubbe himself. There may be other bits of unrecognized truth in his improbable tale; certainly such a possibility cannot be ruled out.

The following version represents my own best guess as to the probable events of Grubbe's life between his leaving Valparaiso in the spring of 1895, and his developing radiation dermatitis in the winter of 1895–96.

Medical school had been Emil's objective since he first enrolled at Normal College, but there was always the necessity of earning his living as he went along. In Valparaiso this had been accomplished by working as night watchman and husbanding the money he earned at various jobs during summer vacations, jobs which included working for Mr. Small, the assayer; serving as a court reporter; and writing copy for patent medicine concerns. There are newspaper clippings from about this time containing advertisements for "Grubbe's Corn Cure," which presumably provided an additional source of income. He made no subsequent mention of the corn cure, however, and the details of its manufacture remain unknown.

The fall term at Hahnemann opened on Tuesday, September 17, and it is reasonably certain that Emil served as an assistant to Professor E. M. Bruce in his physiological chemistry class, which met at 11:30 on Fridays, because there is preserved his course notebook, with grades for fifty-one students, ranging alphabetically from Mrs. Axtell to Mrs. West, with two "R" names added at the end of the list. One student's name is followed by the notation "died," and several of the names listed in the book do not appear in the school catalogue's list of matriculants. Also, nowhere in the catalogue does Emil's name appear as either student or staff member. Professor Bruce had two associates that year, Adjunct Professor M. J. Moth and Lecturer A. F. Storke, who in addition taught Latin and Prescription Writing, but Emil's participation had not yet earned him academic status. Perhaps he was more nearly a *Diener* during the first year.

I have not been able to locate a catalogue for the two academic years 1896–97 and 1897–98, but by 1898–99, Emil had succeeded to the position of "Lecturer on Chemistry" (A. F. Storke having now advanced to the Adjunct Professorship of Materia Medica), and in addition he was listed as an 1897–98 matriculant. The time schedule shows him in charge of two first-year classes (Mondays and Saturdays from 9:30 to 10:30), and he has pencil-checked the first section of the chemical laboratory session on Fridays, possibly to indicate that he had responsibilities there as well. He graduated with the M.D. degree in March, 1898; four years attendance was required, but entering students holding college degrees could be admitted directly to the second year of medical school, which makes it reasonable to assume that he entered the second-year class. He may have entered too late to have his name appear in the student list in the 1895–96 catalogue, and it is probable that his work as an assistant to Professor Bruce did not earn him a

27

place among the faculty until later, presumably in the following year.

It is quite certain that in the Hahnemann environment Grubbe would learn of Roentgen's work. The discovery may have been discussed immediately before, during, or after Dr. J. E. Gilman's materia medica class which met at 9:30 A.M. on Monday, January 6.

Small Crookes tubes, Geissler tubes, and battery-operated induction coils were commonplace in the primitive high-school and college physics laboratories of the day. Emil may have built an induction coil for some purpose or other, or he may have acquired one along with the assay office equipment he purchased from the estate of Mr. Small.

Perhaps there was an Albert Schmidt, someone who helped run the assaying office while Emil worked in the Chemistry Department at Hahnemann and attended classes there; perhaps he joined in "experiments" with the exciting new rays, as hundreds of others were doing throughout the United States and elsewhere in the world. Many other workers suffered from dermatitis such as Emil's, but he may have been unique in having his lesions brought promptly to the attention of physicians, and particularly physicians schooled in the concept *similia similibus curantur*.

That Emil was not yet a physician when he began his primitive radiological experimentation fits neatly into the picture. Roentgen was a physicist, and for several months after his announcement it was mostly physicists and engineers who worked with the rays, making such work their principal business for the time being and thus acquiring cumulative exposures larger than those incurred by physicians, for whom work with X-rays was incidental to other work and interests. Most physician-victims developed lesions more slowly, although there was a particular spurt in frequency of injuries after the clinical use of radium had become established. Emil believed firmly that his undergraduate normal-college courses in chemistry and physics made him a professional in both fields; and as yet there had been little opportunity for him to become involved in biological matters. If he began exposing his hands to X-rays shortly after January 6, 1896, and continued to do so almost daily thereafter for many hours at a time and with extremely short tube-skin distances, as he appears to have done, there was adequate time for the appearance of a severe dermatitis

28

by Monday, January 27, 1896. The fact that on that day his bandage was first noticed by teachers with whom he was in daily contact suggests that he had not worn one previously.

Although Emil lived on into the second half of this century, most of his clinical work and the bulk of his professional writing belong to a quite different period. Advertising was in its clumsy, ebullient infancy then and, while the professional ethics of medical men do not change according to fashion, an elastic attitude toward the real significance of the printed word allowed a certain latitude of utterance. Younger readers may be helped to at least a partial appreciation of conditions in that bygone day by abstracts from some of the fragile, yellowed newspapers of 1896 which I have consulted in connection with this biography.

Dutch-British friction in Africa was an old story, but in 1895 it was about to explode into what we now call the Boer War. Venezuela was unfriendly to the Pope. Cuba was aflame with revolution. The "Terrible Turk" was massacring Armenians, and Japan had a minor local war with the Hakka tribes in newly acquired Formosa. One hopeful sign in a troubled world was a lessening of tension between Kaiser Wilhelm's Prussia and Queen Victoria's England.

Gold mining boomed in Idaho, and the rush was on to Alaska. Eighteen ninety-five was a good year for prize fights and the Democratic Party decided to hold its next convention in Chicago.

Locally, the leap year 1896 turned very cold, assuring a thick cover of ice on the lake, but an impending strike of ice cutters threatened privation for Chicagoans who relished their cool beer on a warm day. True, the great packing plants in the stockyards and the breweries had their own large, steam-powered ammonia gas refrigerating systems, and artificial block ice was not unknown, but it was largely the natural product, cut off the lake in the winter and stored in sawdust until summer, that was peddled from door to door in horsedrawn wagons and was depended on to stock the iceboxes of the householder and the corner saloonkeeper.

Atgeld and Stevenson were getting together. It was thought that labor factions were not likely to unite; there was more trouble for park policemen and teachers' salaries had been cut.

A billiard tournament opened well. A scheme was developed to

29

attract visitors to Chicago, and the city possessed adequate gold to pay off maturing bonds. May wheat was booming, but street railway stocks had declined, and the city's druggists were waging a price war.

At first glance, two feature stories appear to deal with X-rays, but this is not the case. One, entitled, "Where the Sparks Fly," turns out to be an advertisement masquerading as news, praising a Dr. Copeland's ability to restore to full health all of his patients. It includes a testimonal from a Mr. Henry Smith of Chicago, who was cured of asthma by Dr. Copeland and considered him the greatest living specialist. In his testimonial, Mr. Smith predicted the development of "flying machines" and a system he called *televide*, which would enable Dr. Copeland to sit in his State Street office and look into sickrooms 500 miles away.

The second story, headed "Wizard Nikola Tesla and His Wonderful Discovery," tells how Tesla, by shocking the body more than 100 times per second, can deliver in mere seconds the health-giving effects of many hours of horseback riding, curing all diseases except consumption.

Arend's Drug Store offered beef-iron and wine at $1.20 a quart. Paine's Celery Compound had enabled a Mrs. Grinnell to reach the tidy age of 99, and fire chiefs and prominent businessmen lent their names and faces to extol its virtues. "Battle Ax" chewing tobacco was truly the largest piece of fine tobacco ever offered for ten cents, which message was driven home day after day with large, illustrated spreads.

Department stores offered dresses and skirts for from $1.98 to $6.98, pleated and ruffled cotton drawers for 50 cents, and women's heavy rib fleece balbriggan vests and drawers (daringly illustrated on a mannikin), a 75-cent value, for 50 cents. Ladies' fine boots were $2.75 and boys' fine overcoats $5, $8, and $12.

Like the styles and prices of clothing, public attitudes toward exaggeration, misrepresentation, and falsehood in advertising have changed with the passage of seven decades. We still exaggerate, misrepresent, and lie in print, but we do so with a finesse compared to which the 1895 examples appear crude indeed. This evolution in mores should be borne in mind by everyone reading Emil's story.

Four

CAREERS PUBLIC AND PRIVATE

Homeopathy had seen its best days when Emil enrolled at Hahnemann, but it would have required discernment far greater than his to perceive that within a few years homeopathic degrees would lose prestige to the point where many who possessed them took steps to acquire M.D.'s of the regular sort. In 1895, thirty-six years after its establishment, Hahnemann Medical College of Chicago gave only lip service to the basic tenets of its illustrious namesake and had become merely another among the many low-grade schools of the city.

The Flexner Report to which reference has been made was published by the Carnegie Foundation in 1910. The foundation had undertaken a survey and report on medical schools as part of a broader plan to evaluate colleges and universities preparatory to embarking on a program of improving conditions of academic employment. Abraham Flexner, a Louisville educator, was chosen for the job because of the brilliant critique of American universities which he had recently published (1908).

Based on a two-year study of American and Canadian medical schools, the Report caused consternation among medical educators and their political and financial supporters. Doing much of the work himself, and supervising all of it, Flexner investigated and reported on 150 institutions, including not only those considered "regular" but also sectarian schools of homeopathy, eclectic medicine, and osteopathy. Here and there, in connection with the best of the universities, conditions were found to be reasonably good; but the ratio of bad to good was impressively large. Within a few decades, the report led to the elimination of many poor schools and the academic and financial strengthening of those which continued to operate.

Abraham Flexner proved to be the right man in the right place at the right time; it has been said of him that thousands of men and women who have never heard his name owe their health and even their lives to developments that grew directly from the work of this dedicated man, whose M.D. degree was an honorary one, granted late in life.

If the bitter things Flexner had to say about much of the medical education in the first decade of this century caused only anguish among medical educators, they had a quite different effect on wealthy benefactors. John D. Rockefeller, Sr., the Whitneys, George Eastman, Julius Rosenwald, and scores of others, on being provided with the shocking facts, poured out millions of gold-standard dollars for medical education. Flexner was made an officer of the General Education Board of the Rockefeller Foundation. By the time he had left that work to move on to other fields, including the establishment of the Institute for Advanced Studies at Princeton, it is estimated that Abraham Flexner had been instrumental in obtaining more than one-half billion dollars for the rehabilitation of medical education.

Summing up the situation in Illinois, Flexner said:

> The city of Chicago is in respect to medical education the plague spot of the country. The state law is fairly adequate, for it empowers the board of health to establish a standard of preliminary education, laboratory equipment, and clinical facilities, thus fixing the conditions which shall entitle a school to be considered reputable. In pursuance of these powers, the board has made the four-year high school or its equivalent the basis, and has enumerated the essentials of the medical course, including, among other things, clinical instruction through two annual terms.
>
> With the indubitable connivance of the state board, these provisions are, and have been, flagrantly violated. Of the fourteen undergraduate medical schools . . . described, the majority exist and prepare candidates for the Illinois state board examinations in unmistakable contravention of the law and the state board rules. These schools are as follows: (1) Chicago College of Medicine and Surgery (Valparaiso University), (2) Hahnemann Medical College, (3) Hering Medical College, (4) Illinois Medical College, (5) Bennett Medical College, (6) Physio-Medical College of Medicine and Surgery, (7) Jenner Medical College, (8) National Medical University, (9) Reliance Medical College, (10) Littlejohn College of Osteopathy. Of these, only

one, the National Medical University, has been deprived of "good standing" by the board. Without exception, a large proportion of their attendance offers for admission an "equivalent," which is not an equivalent in any sense whatsoever; it is nevertheless accepted without question by the state board, though the statute explicitly states that it can exact an equivalent by "satisfactory" examination. In the case of the night schools,[1] for instance, one or two years' requirements are satisfied by "coaching" one night a week in each of the several subjects: one evening is devoted to Latin, the next to English, the next to mathematics. There is absolutely no guarantee that the candidate accepted on the equivalent basis has had an education even remotely resembling the high school training which the Illinois law intends as the minimum upon which it will recognize a candidate for the physician's license. If the state board should—as in duty bound—publicly brand these schools as "not in good standing" by reason of their failure to require a suitable preliminary education of their students, their graduates would be immediately excluded from practice in Illinois; adjoining states would rapidly follow suit, with the result that the schools would shortly be exterminated. Fortunately, the case against them does not rest alone on the question of entrance requirements: for not a single one of the schools mentioned furnishes clinical opportunities in proper abundance, and some of them even fail to provide the stipulated training in other branches, e.g., anatomy. An efficient and intelligent administration of the law would thus reduce in short order the medical schools of Chicago to three, Rush, Northwestern, and the College of Physicians and Surgeons.[2]

---

[1] Even supposing the night schools enforced an entrance standard and actually provided laboratories and hospitals of the right kind, the teaching of anything but didactic medicine at night is practically impossible because: (1) the time is too limited. The day school is in operation all day long, and the student has his evenings for study; the night school can at most secure three or four hours when the student is already physically fatigued. (2) Laboratory work by artificial light is bound to be unsatisfactory, even if the lighting is good, which is not usually the case. (3) Hospital clinics, operations, etc., must be very limited at night, when the interest of the patient requires that he be allowed to rest. Children's diseases cannot be studied at night at all. (4) The situation is rendered even more absurd by the fact, that, in addition to all these handicaps, the night school frequently has to make up some conditions in preliminary studies.

[2] For the American Medical Missionary College, see "Michigan."

Of Hahnemann specifically the report stated (p. 214):

> The school occupies a building wretchedly dirty, except-
> ing only the single laboratory, fairly equipped, devoted to
> pathology and bacteriology. The equipment covers in a
> meager way also anatomy, physiology, histology, and chem-
> istry.
> In the adjoining hospital there are accommodations in
> the wards for sixty beds, but there are no ward clinics. The
> superintendent is a layman who "does not believe in ad-
> mitting students to the wards." There is no regular way for
> them to see common acute disease as "only amphitheater
> clinics are held." Hospital interns do all the obstetrical
> work; students "look on." The school also holds two ap-
> pointments on the surgical side in the Cook County Hos-
> pital. There is a fair dispensary.

When Emil Grubbe graduated from Hahnemann in March,
1898, he was rather a "second-class" physician in his great and
growing home town, and the medical circles in which he moved
were fixed. His path seldom crossed those of such men as Fenger,
Senn, Herrick, Hektoen, and scores of other giants who were making medical history on Chicago's West Side. His friends and
professional associates included a few who were superior to their
environment, but only a few. Some of them enrolled in regular
schools, and at least as early as 1919, Emil was claiming that he
had, in 1911, received an additional M.D. degree from the Chicago College of Medicine and Surgery, at various times the medical department of Valparaiso or Loyola. If he ever did receive such
a degree, he did not preserve the diploma nor register it with the
state of Illinois, and the officers of the two universities concerned
did not record the degree. It is hard to understand why he did
not, in fact, avail himself of such an opportunity. Grubbe was
Professor and Head of the Department of Electro-Therapy at
Chicago College of Medicine and Surgery, and since that institution, formerly "eclectic," had few if any entrance requirements
(even for students who had flunked out of other low-grade
schools), for a member of its own faculty, even such requirements
as existed probably would have been waived.

In the late spring of 1915, the dean of the Chicago College of
Medicine and Surgery notified Emil that he must choose between
that school and Hahnemann, not serve as a faculty member of

both; and shortly thereafter the Chicago College of Medicine and Surgery surrendered its state charter in still another of its many transmutations.

Emil states:

> After my graduation as a physician things changed considerably. Not only the subject of X-rays but I, myself, received quite a good deal of attention. First the subject of X-rays was regarded as of sufficient importance to have it added to the medical college curriculum. Second, I was transferred from the Department of Chemistry and Physics to a new department, that of Roentgenology and Electro-Therapeutics, and so I became a teacher of the X-ray. . . . I now received the title Professor of Roentgenology. To my knowledge this was the first medical school in the world to establish a chair of Roentgenology. Also, as far as I am able to find out, I thus became the first professor of Roentgenology in the world.

Available records dispute this chronology. In the 1899–1900 Hahnemann catalogue there is no mention of X-rays, and E. H. Grubbe, M.D., is listed as "Assistant in Medicine" on the hospital staff. As late as February, 1903, *The Clinique*, house organ of the school, lists him merely as "Professor of Electro-Therapeutics," and only by the year 1904 has the listing become "Professor of Electro-Therapeutics and Radiography."

It is indisputable, however, that "things changed considerably." The following announcement is the first record we have of one such change:

Dr. E. H. Grubbe

Clara Jensen

Married

Monday, September 11

1899

Pentwater, Michigan

At home
After October 20th
2907 Groveland Avenue
Chicago

On it is penciled the notation that the witnesses were Peter Jensen and Olga Davis, and from clippings of the Pentwater newspapers I know that Peter was Clara's brother and Olga her sister.

How Emil came to meet Clara, whether there had been earlier loves, and what was Clara's social, economic, and educational background remain dark; but something Emil said to another woman many years after he had divorced Clara suggests that the bride from Michigan found at 2907 Groveland Avenue, Chicago, a sternly disciplined establishment.

Five days before his marriage, on September 6, 1899, Dr. H. V. Halbert, Professor of Clinical Medicine, wrote to Emil:

> It is settled that you may have a clinic at the College at 10:30 Wednesday. Just what apparatus you will be able to use or what your work will be other than the treatment by electricity of the clinical patients which we will send to you, I cannot yet exactly say. I wish you would confer in regard to this, and then see me at your earliest convenience.

Three years later, E. Stillman Bailey, M.D., dean of the college, wrote that the governing faculty, at its meeting on the previous day (February 5, 1902), had adopted his recommendation and had created a Department of Electro-Therapeutics with Emil Grubbe in full charge, as Professor of Electro-Therapeutics, with power to appoint such assistants as he deemed necessary.

On August 13 of the same year the Registrar, Dr. W. Henry Wilson, wrote Emil offering the services of two students, Laura Brown and Charles De Bois, who were seeking work during the coming year.

For the first six years after graduation, therefore, the work at Hahnemann was not in radiology. Even by 1903, the arrangements for electrotherapy were beginning to call forth criticism from Emil. He complained that the room set aside for his work was deplorably dirty and that apparatus was damaged and even lost because it was employed by others in his absence. On January 22, 1903, Dr. Wilson, the registrar, replied, quoting a January 7 action by the faculty that made Emil the proper custodian of all the electrical apparatus in the institution and reiterating the statement that he had full power to train such assistants as might be needed for the clinical work in the college. The situation does not seem to have improved, however; a penciled note is preserved from which presumably a typewritten reply was prepared. It reads:

To Hahnemann Executive Committee, October 20, 1906. Gentlemen: Due to the fact that the Electrotherapeutic Clinic cannot be conducted under existing conditions both in the interests of the students and patients on the one hand and physicians who have private cases which they desire to treat personally by electric methods on the other hand, I wish to present the subject to your committee for assistance and, if possible, final settlement.

If I remember correctly, the primary object of the establishment of the Electric Clinic was for the purpose of giving the students practical clinical work. Although at the beginning and for some time nothing happened to interfere with the original purpose of the clinic, it seems that lately (during the past two years) the primary object (of the clinic) has been very much overlooked.

Those who have tried to do the clinical work in this department have been considerably handicapped first on account of lack of apparatus (much of the apparatus being stolen about as fast as purchased—even some of my own instruments have been taken); second on account of having to use apparatus damaged by persons who are not competent to handle same; third on account of appropriation of the clinic room by other departments and outside physicians as a result of which the room is very often in an unsanitary condition and at other times a veritable junkshop making it a very unsuitable place for storing existing delicate electrical apparatus.

As a remedy, he proposed the purchase of another complete set of equipment and, in conclusion, threatened to leave the clinical department "unless some radical changes can be brought about."

A year later, Howard R. Chislett, current dean, wrote on November 1, 1907:

Will you please inform me at your earliest convenience whether or not it is your intention to conduct a clinic in Electrotherapeutics this year? For four or five months now there has been no clinic on this present-day important subject, and I am sorry to say that the Electro-Therapeutic Laboratory is absolutely useless as far as any convenience to the hospital or to the attending physicians and surgeons is concerned. We feel that it is just as important that these clinics be continued throughout the entire year as those in medicine and surgery, and if it has become a burden for you to attend to this department, we feel it's your duty either to furnish a substitute when you cannot be here or to make room for someone who has both the time and inclination. The superintendent tells us that the apparatus is now in order.

Emil's reply, dated November 5, 1907, reads,

> Your letter of recent date at hand. In reply will say that the reason why the Electro-Therapeutic Clinic has not yet opened for the school year is because of lack of equipment to conduct a clinic properly. At the opening of the term I looked over what was left of last year's outfit and informed Mr. Burt that a considerable part of the apparatus was either out of order or had been taken away. I was told by him to report to the faculty. I wrote a letter to Dr. Wilson enumerating the articles needed and their probable cost, and since then I have been awaiting results but up to date little or nothing has been done. If the superintendent thinks the apparatus is now in good working order, he has a perfect right to such an opinion; but I fail to see how good clinical work is possible with the present state of the equipment. On October 20, 1906, I wrote the Executive Committee a letter detailing the trials, troubles, and needs of the Electro-Therapeutic Clinic. If this letter is convenient I wish it read again to the Committee as I believe what I said then to be still applicable, since the same circumstances which we had to contend with then still exist. . . .
>
> If anyone can be found who is willing to do this work and at the same time contend with many things which have been my lot, I will be very pleased to be relieved of the job. Under the circumstances I will do as your committee suggests, and I ask to be excused from clinical work in electro-therapeutics.

Half a century later, Dean Chislett's firm reply of November 8, 1907, impresses me as kindly and fair. He wrote,

> Your letter of recent date has been received. I note what you say in relation to the lack of apparatus and have been conscious that the demands made by the Electro-Therapeutic Department have necessarily been much greater than those made by other departments because probably of the delicacy of the instruments. It would, however, seem strange to me that after a course of instruction through the junior year and a course of clinics through the senior year that our graduates should be too ignorant to know how to manage a static machine or an X ray coil.
>
> Several months ago, in fact nearly a year from the pres-

ent time, the Executive Committee passed a rule that a certain member of the intern staff should in your absence be the only one allowed to use the electrical appliances, and you in turn promised to give those interns such instructions as you deemed necessary to enable them to use the apparatus for the benefit of the hospital staff. We have not yet had one intern who seemed to know enough to even start the machine satisfactorily. Whose fault this is I do not know but am painfully aware that for five months now there has been no clinic held in the Electro-Therapeutic Laboratory.

We are sorry if illness in your family has interfered with your proper attendance upon the clinic and should like you to feel that we appreciate the services you have rendered the institution.

If you will notify us of an hour that you can attend regularly and if you will send me a list of the really necessary articles needed, I shall do my best to have them purchased for you. An early reply will oblige. Yours truly, Howard R. Chislett, Dean.

Emil's reply of November 16, 1907, read:

Since I wrote you last I took for granted that my resignation from the clinical work in the department would be accepted and therefore made arrangements to occupy all my time Thursdays and Saturdays, A.M. On this account I can't reconsider the matter even though another hour . . . could be assigned to me.

I have talked with Dr. Kimball about taking charge of the clinic and if agreeable to the faculty she will, after the necessary repairs and instruments have been supplied, be pleased to do this work.

On November 18, 1907, Chislett answered,

Your letter of November 16 has just been received. I will present your resignation from the clinical work in the Electro-Therapeutic Department to the Executive Committee at its next meeting and in the meantime I shall write to Dr. Kimball and ask her to assume the control of the Clinical Department until the Committee can take definite action.

This laborious exchange seems to indicate that the Hahnemann connection was ending, but, as a matter of fact, a dozen years later Emil still was listed in the college catalogue, now as "Professor of Electrology and X-Rayology," and in 1938, long after the demise of the college, the officers of Hahnemann Hospital wrote to him telling him of his recent election to honorary staff membership.

I have reproduced this correspondence because, unlike almost everything else on which this biography must be built, these letters provide straightforward evidence as to what Emil and some of those in contact with him thought and said. Most of the other "papers" are notes written many years after the events with which they deal. Even more important is the fact that these letters show that the professorship and department of "radiology" of which Emil was so proud really had to do with electrology tinged ever so slightly with X-rays.

It is noteworthy that while these events were occurring in Chicago, Sweden was laying the groundwork for what have become the world's finest departments of radiology. There is more than a little doubt whether, in even the most technical sense, Emil's appointment at Hahnemann antedated that of Thor Stenback in Stockholm; certainly, in quality, continuity, and long-range influence the Swedish activity of the closing years of the nineteenth century dwarfs to microscopic proportions that of Grubbe at Hahnemann during the same period.

The situation was even worse at the other schools with which he later became associated: Jenner, Chicago College of Medicine and Surgery, and the General Medical College. The last-named existed briefly in the post-Flexner report period as successor to Hahnemann. Flexner had had this to say of the other two (p. 211):

> Jenner Medical College. A night school occupying three other floors of a business house. Nominal compliance with state law. Clinical facilities are practically nil. An out-and-out commercial enterprise. The institution is plainly a quiz-compend drill aimed at the written examination set up by the State Board of Illinois and of other States.
>
> Chicago College of Medicine and Surgery. . . . Advanced standing has been indiscriminately granted to students who had previously attended low-grade institutions, some of them now defunct. Credit has been allowed to former students of even the worst of the Chicago night schools. . . . There is no protection against fraud or forgery.

Emil's vanity probably was tickled by the addition of these "professorships" to his curriculum vitae, but they could have brought in little money and presumably consisted merely of occasional "lectures."

His real love, exceeding by far his feeling for Hahnemann itself, was for twin activities which he himself had assisted in creating and which he developed and promoted in every possible manner. These apples of his eye were the Illinois X-Ray and Electro-Therapeutic Laboratory and its scarcely-to-be-distinguished alter ego, the Illinois School of Electro-Therapeutics, both located at first in the Champlain Building at the northwest corner of State and Madison streets, opposite Field's where only a few years earlier he had been stockboy and office boy. Of these two activities Emil says,

> I organized and incorporated the Illinois X-Ray and Electro-Therapeutic Laboratory. It was this Laboratory which I established in the Champlain Building in August, 1898. . . . Several of us who specialized in the use of physical agents met to discuss the possibility of teaching this subject to other physicians. . . . Accordingly we organized the Illinois School of Electro-Therapeutics. . . . Space for this school was taken in the same building in which I had my office, namely the Champlain Building. . . . The school was incorporated in May, 1899, by Charles S. Neiswanger, Franklin H. Martin, and Emil H. Grubbe, and I became vice-president and Professor of Radiography, X-ray therapy, and electrophysics. . . . The disruption of the post-graduate medical teaching produced by World War I was the cause of closing this school in 1920. During its twenty-one years of existence, the school had more than 5,000 students.

It is not to be wondered that these statements, made almost a half-century after the event, should be somewhat inaccurate as to dates and other details, but inaccurate chronology occurs as well in contemporary announcements and booklets of the school.

The records of the State of Illinois reveal the following: The Illinois School of Electro-Therapeutics was incorporated April 14, 1900 (*not* May, 1899), with a capital stock of $20,000 consisting of 2,000 shares at $10.00 a share by A. B. Slater, C. E. Heckler, and G. Shadbolt; it was dissolved October 25, 1926.

On April 9, 1900, Dr. Neiswanger from his office in the Marshall Field Building had written to Emil at 26th and Cottage Grove:

> Dear Dr. The scheme which I spoke to you about some time ago has materialized, and I should like to confer with you at your earliest convenience to make all necessary arrangements. The school has been incorporated, and everything is on a good basis.

The discrepancy between the dates April 9 and April 14 presumably means merely that there was a lapse of a few days between filing and recording the fact that an incorporation had been accomplished. The annual report, filed January 17, 1902, listed as officers C. S. Neiswanger, M.D., president; A. B. Slater, secretary-treasurer; and E. H. Grubbe, vice-president.

On Saturday, May 12, 1900, Neiswanger wrote again, this time on the stationery of the new school and directing his note merely to "Dr. Emil H. Grubbe, City."

> Dear Dr. Our schedule gives you the honor of opening the "Illinois School of Electro-Therapeutics" from 10:00 to 12:00 on Monday, May 14th. I do not know how many scholars there will be, but be sure and be on time at that time. Yours very truly, C. H. Neiswanger.

It is with this note that the contemporary inconsistencies begin. The 1900 letterhead lists Emil as vice-president two years before the official records accord him that title and at a time when H. T. Fisher was listed as vice-president in the official records in Springfield. On April 17, 1901, Mr. Slater's circular letter says that the school has just entered the second year of its existence, but sometime in the fall of 1900 he had sent out an "important notice" saying, among other things, that on May 1, 1901, the school would have completed its first year's work. On September 16, 1903, there was prepared for Neiswanger's signature a form letter including the statement, "We are now nearing the completion of our fifth year." In cold fact, May 14, 1905, would be the fifth anniversary.

Two days before the official date of the corporation, Slater and Neiswanger sold Emil 50 shares of the $10.00 stock. In 1902 he bought from Slater 100 shares that were in his name and in 1904 additional shares which the latter had purchased earlier from an S. V. Clevenger.

There was a reorganization of the school in 1904, with Slater stepping out and selling the bulk of his stock to a Joseph P. Foster.

In his farewell letter, Slater thanked Emil for kind co-operation and support and said he was resigning because of illness.

More than a dozen years later, on February 14, 1917, Neiswanger summoned Emil to a meeting of stockholders to consider reduction in the amount of capital stock. Emil has told us that World War I brought evil days for the school, and even though dissolution of the corporation did not come until 1926, the absence of booklets and advertisements subsequent to 1919 indicates that at least as far as Emil was concerned the end came almost a decade before legal recognition of that fact.

But trouble had plagued the school from its opening year, as evidenced by a form letter signed by Dr. Neiswanger some time in 1900.

> Dear Dr.: In calling your attention to the enclosed announcement of the Illinois School of Electro-Therapeutics we are not unmindful of the fact that the imperfect teaching of this subject in the past has done much to bring discredit and adverse criticisms upon this most valuable therapeutic adjunct.
>
> While we shall pass these criticisms in silence—because they emanate from those who understand the subject the least—we shall aim to remedy all past defects in teaching, and the selection of our faculty goes to prove that we have made the most important step in that direction. They are all men of well-known ability. A two weeks course will make you self dependent. Yours very truly, C. S. Neiswanger.

In 1904 Slater had said to Emil that his resignation was necessitated by ill health, but a circular form letter to customers sent out in that year by the new secretary, W. H. Knapp, indicates that Slater's illness was merely diplomatic. Slater had been financially interested in a company manufacturing electrotherapeutic equipment; and this fact had led to a feeling among dealers and other manufacturers that the school was a mere commercial affair.

There was trouble also with the curriculum. At the outset, Emil was committed to two hours Monday mornings and one hour for the remaining mornings, including Saturdays, week in and week out for the entire year; Dr. Rice for almost as much time; and others for only slightly less. After a few months such a schedule was found to be altogether too irksome, aside from reducing time for private practice, so it was amended by interposing a free week between succeeding three-week terms.

In the fall of 1903 the school moved from the thirteenth floor of the Champlain Building to new quarters on the fourth floor of the Atlas block, 35 East Randolph. Simultaneously, Emil moved his private practice from the eighth floor of the Champlain Building to the second floor of the Butler Building, then at 52 South State Street, now 160 North State Street.

The Illinois X-Ray and Electro-Therapeutic Laboratory was incorporated June 1, 1901 (*not* August, 1898), with a capital stock of $25,000 consisting of 250 shares at $100 each. The incorporators were John E. Gilman, Emil H. Grubbe, and Richard H. Street (*not* Emil alone). Reports were filed for the years 1902–4 but not for 1905, and on March 1, 1904, President E. H. Grubbe signed a request for voluntary dissolution of the corporation. The 1902–3 reports showed Gilman, president; Street, secretary-treasurer; and Grubbe, vice-president. In the 1904 report, Emil was president; his wife, Clara, secretary; and L. M. Jensen (her father?), treasurer.

It is noteworthy that although the school began to languish about 1917, its corporate existence continued for another decade, while Emil's office, which he continued until his retirement in 1947, ceased to be a corporation in 1905. No facts are available, but my guess is that as Emil's reputation grew to the point where he no longer needed the moral, professional, and financial assistance of others, he set up shop for himself and had no further need for corporate status. I suspect that after he had bought out the other members of the laboratory corporation, he overlooked the necessity of making a yearly report to Springfield until crowded by the state and then, improvising the necessary officers, made a final report, and dissolved the corporation.

Throughout the period in the Champlain Building and for at least part of the time in the Butler Building, Emil continued to operate the old laboratory at 2614 Cottage Grove, which he had opened before he graduated from medical school.

In the year 1900 the course at the Illinois School of Electro-Therapeutics lasted two weeks and tuition was $25.00, but by 1903 the course had been lengthened to three weeks and the fee raised to $40.00. From time to time, special two-week courses were offered at the old fee. Statements among Emil's notes indicate that in addition to serving as vice-president and professor of X-ray physics and radiotherapy, he wrote the literature for the school. Typical of many others preserved among his papers are "Bulletin of Information," No. 3, issued during the summer of 1900, and the following two pages from another document, presumably vintage 1901:

A born physicist and teacher, the envy of many older in years, are the attributes of our Vice-president, who has been identified with the school since its inception. The field of work in his care needs but little review. His teachings are so thorough that all learn valuable technique in administering X-Rays for therapeutic and diagnostic purposes.

With the application of X-Rays to medicine commenced the remarkable improvements in appliances for generating this force with which we work so familiarly to-day. Advances have been made very rapidly, and many advantages are offered to the physician and surgeon in arriving at a correct diagnosis in obscure cases, which were not accorded him a few years ago.

Because of the ever increasing popularity of this branch of electricity for its diagnostic as well as its therapeutic possibilities, we are more active than ever in supplying instruction in this department. We are well equipped and endeavor to make the student proficient in the examination of the heart, lungs, stomach, liver, brain, fractures, and dislocations; to locate foreign bodies in any part of the body. Besides, the student is taught the care of the machine, the selection and handling of the Crookes tubes, and the various other minutia necessary to make a successful operator in this branch.

In applying the X-Rays to the human body for the purpose of making a diagnosis we may use one or two methods, namely: Fluoroscopy or Radiography.

Fluoroscopic examinations are made by exciting the Crooke's tube and placing the part of the body to be examined between a chemically treated piece of paper enclosed in a box called a Fluoroscope and the tube. By this method we can "see" with our own eyes and thus make a comparative study of conditions. However, the fluoroscopic method has many drawbacks and is not generally to be recommended. Its greatest disadvantage is the fact that we only get a temporary picture and also that it takes an expert to interpret correctly the results. A much better and, at the same time, permanent method of X-Ray examination is by the Radiographic method. In the use of this method we call in ordinary photographic processes to aid us.

Among the conditions demonstrable by the X-Ray by means of Radiographs may be mentioned: Fractures, dislocations, tumors, and abnormal growths, bone diseases, stone in the kidney, bladder, and gall bladder, diseases of the heart and lungs, deformities of the spine and hip, floating kidney, gout, aneurism, joint diseases, bullets, needles, and other foreign bodies. The X-Ray is also used in determining the extent of congenital dislocation of the hip.

The stomach may be definitely outlined and its size, shape, and position determined. In short, the X-Ray is a medium capable of being used for diagnosing many diseases in which physical signs are very doubtful and many times absent. The X-Ray is also used extensively in medico-legal procedures. For instance, in observing fractures, determining fractures from dislocations, determining the presence and location of bullets, and differential diagnosis of various kinds. To-day it is a very common thing to call in the X-Ray expert in cases of litigation, and many cases are settled almost wholly on the strength of the X-Ray evidence submitted.

The use of the X-Ray as a therapeutic agent is at present well established. Its phenomenal success as a curative agent in carcinoma, lupus, eczema, chronic ulcers, and pulmonary tuberculosis has opened up an enormous field wherein the general practitioner may well devote his time.

Under its influence, combined with constitutional treatment, numerous cases of consumption may be decidedly benefited, and many have been actually cured. The same may be said for tuberculosis of the bones. Among the other diseases in which X-Ray treatments have given good results may be mentioned: The various kinds of acne, sycosis, herpes, hypertrichosis, favus, chronic oedema, tubercular glands, birthmarks, moles, scars due to burns or scalds, varicose veins. Hair may also be removed by it.

The question of "X-Ray burns" is carefully considered, the whole subject being taken up in detail.

At present every physician who wishes to be "up to date" should be conversant with X-Ray methods, for, if he omits this knowledge, he is simply standing in his own light.

In this branch, as in all other subjects, we instruct the student by methods peculiarly our own. All points of interest and value are brought out with such clearness as to make it plain to everyone.

The didactic instruction in this department covers the

Albert Grubbe, father of Emil, in 1894
at age 52.

Bertha Grubbe, mother of Emil, in
1894, at age 51.

Photograph made of Grubbe at age 17 in Valparaiso, Indiana, during the first year of his attendance at Northern Indiana Normal School as a student of science and pharmacy.

At 21, Grubbe had been less than a year out of Normal School. He was at that time a professional assayer, chemistry teacher, and first-year medical student at Hahnemann. It was also at this time that Dr. Ludlam and Dr. Halphide sent the first patients to him for X-ray treatment.

When he was 26 years old and three years out of medical school, Emil had become part owner and vice-president of the Illinois School of Electro-Therapeutics. He wrote the copy for that institution's numerous brochures, including the one which carried this photograph and the legend:

A born physicist and teacher, the envy of many older in years, are the attributes of our vice-president who has been identified with the school since its inception. The field of work in his care (Radiography, X-ray Therapeutics, and Electrophysics) needs but little review so thorough are his teachings. All learn valuable technique in administering to patients the various forms of X-ray for therapeutic and surgical purposes.

Clara Jensen Grubbe. Married September 11, 1899, at Pentwater, Michigan. Divorced March 6, 1911, in Chicago.

Grubbe home at 2907 Groveland Avenue, Chicago (later Ellis), in 1899. Here the newlyweds lived with their servant, Anna Lindquist, until they moved to Indiana Avenue. Like many other physicians during the period of the city's vigorous growth, Dr. Grubbe found it profitable to augment his income from practice by speculation in Chicago real estate and in mining stock.

Dr. Grubbe in his electric automobile in
1898, the year of his graduation from Hahnemann. Car bore number 42.

Grubbe's sister poses in the automobile.

that does not give you the same confidence as seeing it applied by an experienced operator or doing it yourself under his guidance.

The principal drawback with physicians in the therapeutic use of electricity seems to be to commence the study of it from the wrong end. They purchase an elaborate electro-therapeutic outfit, about which they know nothing except the mechanical manipulation of the switches, and expect to use, as a curative agent, this most potent of all nature's remedies; they seem to forget that the amputating case does not make the surgeon.

Advantage of Clinical Teaching.

Ignorance on the part of the profession only demonstrates the importance of such an institution as the Illinois School of Electro-Therapeutics.

It is supplied with abundant clinical material, and no attempt is made to treat cases by electricity which could be more successfully cured by other means.

The student at this school notes the careful technique observed; he is convinced that it *does* matter in applying galvanism whether the positive or negative pole is used; that it makes a difference whether treatment is continued for ten minutes when the condition indicates five; that the kind of current, whether static, galvanic, faradic or sinusoidal used in a particular case determines success or failure.

Students in some of the classes have been surprised to see cases of endometritis almost cured by four simple treatments; extensive erosions, which have resisted months of treatment by usual methods, cured in a much shorter time by cupric electrolysis. Their astonishment was no less to see hay fever of regular yearly recurrence from August until October entirely disappear after six or eight treatments.

Cases of neuritis are quickly benefited, and in one instance an ulnar neuritis of eight months duration was permanently relieved by a single application of static surgings.

Such results as these are opening the eyes of the medical profession to the great future in store for this therapeutic agent.

Is Medical Electricity a Fad?

When we surround a subject with mystery we are never able to study it rationally, and ever since the day when Thales rubbed amber into "life" electrical phenomena has been viewed with awe and surrounded by so much mystery as to absolutely forbid its proper study.

A page from the *Bulletin* of the Illinois School of Electro-Therapy.

Dr. Grubbe's reception room. (From the *Bulletin* of the Illinois School of Electro-Therapy.)

Dr. Emil H. Grubbe in September, 1951, at age 77, nine years before his death. His left hand and wrist had been amputated in 1929 following an automobile accident. Lesions are apparent on his right hand and on his face.

Advertisement for Grubbe's laboratory which appeared in the *Osteopathic Physician.*

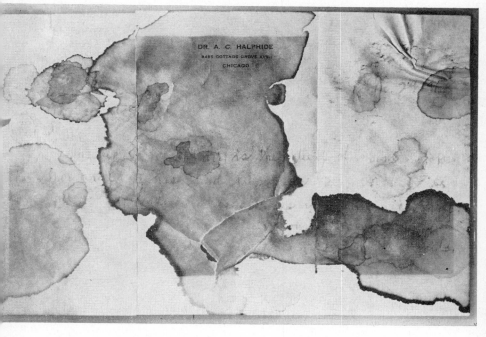

This letter from Dr. Ludlam about a carcinoma patient verifies Emil's claims that other doctors sent patients to him. (Courtesy of the Smithsonian Institution.)

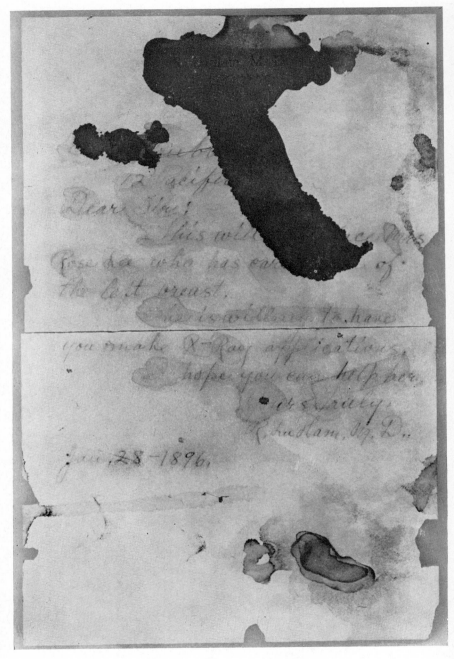

Letter from Dr. Halphide whose patient Grubbe treated. This letter and Dr. Ludlam's letter constitute the only documents tending to validate the truth of Emil's assertions. (Courtesy of the Smithsonian Institution.)

DIPLOMA.

SCIENTIFIC DEPARTMENT,

Northern Indiana Normal School.

VALPARAISO, IND.

To whom this may come greeting:

Be it known that *Emil H. Grube* this day has completed at this Institution the Scientific Course of Study, and his attainments in that regard being satisfactory; we do now confer upon him the Degree of *Bachelor of Science*.

In Witness whereof the said Northern Indiana Normal School has caused these presents to be signed by its President and Department Instructors and attested by its Secretary and the Corporate seal to be hereto affixed.

this _15th_ day of _Aug_ 1895.

H. B. Brown
President.

J. B. Lesh
Secretary.

Department Instructors:

Higher Mathematics _M. E. Bogarte_
Natural Science _H. N. Crane_
Latin Language _H. N. Crane_
German Language _J. E. Roessler_
English Literature _O. P. Kinsey_

DIPLOMA

PHARMACY DEPARTMENT,

Northern Indiana Normal School,

VALPARAISO, INDIANA.

To whom this may come greeting:

Emit H. Grubbe this day has completed at this Institution the Pharmacy Course of Study and his attainments in that regard being satisfactory; we do now confer upon him the Degree of Graduate of Pharmacy.

In Witness whereof the said Northern Indiana Normal School has caused these presents to be signed by its President, and Department Instructors and attested by its Secretary and the Corporate seal to be there affixed this 15th day of August 1895.

F. B. Brown _____ G. Black
President _____ Secretary.

Faculty:

S. W. Bar — Professor of Pharmacy;

_____ — Professor of Chemistry;

_____ — Professor of Botany;

_____ — Professor of Physiology;

W. H. Cann — Professor of Latin;

_____ — Professor of Therapeutics.

Hahnemann Medical College and Hospital

OF CHICAGO.

The Board of Trustees of the

Hahnemann Medical College on the recommendation of the Faculty has conferred the Degree of

DOCTOR OF MEDICINE AND SURGERY,

with all the rights and privileges thereunto belonging, on

E. H. Grubbe, B. S.

who has completed the course of study prescribed by this College.

In testimony whereof this DIPLOMA is given in the City of Chicago, State of Illinois, U.S.A.
this twenty-fourth day of March, 1898.

C. Stifloot, M.D. Dean of the Faculty.

R. Ludlam, M.D., President.

FACULTY:

R. Ludlam, M.D. Prof. Surgical Gynecology
C. Stifloot M.D. Prof. Obstetrics & Medical Jurisprudence
Fulton French, M.D. Prof. of Obstetrics
E. S. Bailey, M.D. Prof. Medical Gynecology
J. H. Gibson M.D. Senior Prof. of Surgery
A. L. Grayson M.D. Prof. Nervous Diseases
J. E. Johnson M.D. Prof. Materia Medica Therap.

N. Halsted M.D. Prof. of Anatomy
E. H. Armstrong M.D. Prof. of Theory & Practice
J. S. Mitchell M.D. Prof. of Physiology
Paul Welch M.D. Prof. of Chem & Tox.
Leander Young M.D. Prof. of Surgery
Philip A. Dunn M.B. Prof. Laryngology & Rhinology
Clarence Peterson M.D. Prof. Ophthalmology
Oliver S. Haywood M.D. Prof. of Anatomy

The Illinois

X-Ray and Electro-Therapeutic Laboratory

OF CHICAGO

INCORPORATED.

THE UNDERSIGNED HEREBY CERTIFIES THAT

Emil H. Grubbé, B. S., M. D.

has attended a private course in X-Ray and Electro-Therapeutic work in this Laboratory and has shown evidence of proficiency. In Testimony Whereof, I have conferred upon him this Certificate and affixed thereto my signature and the Corporate Seal at Chicago, Illinois, this twelfth day of January, A. D. nineteen hundred and three.

Emil H. Grubbé, M. D.
President.

following: Rudimentary physics, X-Ray tubes, X-Ray generation, fluoroscopic method of using the X-Ray, Radio-
therapeutics. Clinically many applications for the X-Ray
will be found.

The "laboratory" flourished too. At first it was a joint activity
of Gilman, Grubbe, and Street, with hours from 10:00 A.M. to
4:00 P.M. and facilities for fluoroscopy, radiography, radio therapeutic treatment (the tautology persists in some quarters even
today), and electric treatments, static, galvanic, and faradic, at
fees ranging from $3.00 to $25.00. Later, when Emil became sole
proprietor, office hours were restricted to afternoons and fees were
raised somewhat.

The laboratory corporation had a lively appreciation of the value
of advertising, whether of the free variety, which was to be had in
journalistic coverage of patients who were socially important or
newsworthy for other reasons, or of the variety that was for sale
in the advertising columns of medical publications, including the
Osteopathic Physician.[3]

On Monday, August 25, 1902, when the laboratory corporation
was a little more than a year old, Emil wrote to his vacationing
partner, Richard Street,

> Simply swamped. Radio busi. very good. Have one or
> more everyday. Don't get through until after five. Hope
> you can get back by Sat. Would like to take a week's va-
> cation as the school term has been shortened one week to
> give us all a chance. Average 85.00 [$85.00?] per day. New
> ones come everyday. Gilman says your father wrote him
> you were worrying over the Lab. Don't worry. Alic & I are
> running the joint quite smoothly. I have deposited
> $480.00.

This penciled draft, from which presumably a letter was prepared, was made on the address side of a one-cent postal card,
carrying in its upper right-hand corner a likeness of the recently
assassinated President McKinley, and in the left the seal of the Post
Office Department. The card had been mailed in Chicago at 5:30
P.M. on Wednesday, August 20, 1902, by the office of Dr. Spald-
ing and was a notification that the Commissioner of Health had
appointed Emil public vaccinator for the Mosley and South Divi-

---

[3] See Appendix I.

sion High Schools, and requested him to call at Room 2, City Hall, to receive instructions and supplies.

Teacher at four institutions; proprietor of one private office and for a while of two; conductor of a clinic at Hahnemann Hospital; one might think these activities enough of a load for any man, but Emil thought otherwise. This service as vaccinator in two Chicago high schools was only one of several additional jobs. He continued to write copy for the brochures of electrical manufacturers and drug houses but apparently lacked the time for careful proofreading, as evidenced by the fact that in one of several such booklets preserved in his scrapbook the radiograph of a knee with metallic fragments in it is printed upside down and labeled "showing buck-shot in arm." The "buck-shot" one must excuse, because physicians who are unacquainted with firearms commonly call all such fragments "shot" and all shot "buck-shot"; but it did not take a physician, much less a radiologist, to note the mistake in anatomy and the inversion of the reproduced radiograph. Those errors must be attributed to the harassment of overwork.

Another booklet, for C. Birtman and Company, 1907, was an enthusiastic description of that manufacturer's apparatus for generating "pure ozone" uncontaminated by decomposition products. Ozone gas, said Emil, was a most potent remedy for Hodgkin's disease, syphilis, tuberculosis, bronchitis, pneumonia, asthma, hay fever, catarrh, coryza, pharyngitis, rheumatism, auto-intoxication, arteriosclerosis, rickets, menstrual disorders, stomach disorder, and nervous diseases, and as a tonic for blood, metabolism, and lymph. In this remarkable instrument, the ozone was absorbed in oil which was nebulized for inhalation, and the ozone-loaded oil remaining in the nebulizer cup at the end of a day's run could be removed and applied locally to various skin lesions, including varicose ulcers. The price for a machine capable of treating two patients simultaneously was $275 and for a four-patient model $375, plus $75.00 if the machine had to operate on direct current. Testimonials from four customers indicated complete professional and financial satisfaction with the instruments.

Work such as this may have been done during night hours which, in those days, had not yet been pre-empted by radio and television; but there were numerous daytime extracurricular activities as well. In addition to Hahnemann, six other hospitals saw him occasionally as a specialist in radiotherapy. One of these was the Pine Sanitorium, a deluxe institution for alcoholics and drug addicts operated by Dr. Milton B. Pine in a lavish Prairie Avenue building, previously the home of the late Marshall Field, Emil's boyhood employer; and another was the Gilman X-Ray Sanitarium in Peekskill, New York.

On January 20, 1902, Dr. John Gilmaan contracted with Stephen F. Horton of Peekskill to establish in that city a sanitarium for the treatment of cancer by a special method devised by Gilman. He agreed to instruct Horton in the current Gilman methods and in such new developments as might be made, but stipulated that Horton not divulge the secret method to others or employ it clinically anywhere except at the new institution, where fees would be credited to the sanitarium corporation in which Gilman had a 55 per cent interest. Half of this stock Gilman promptly sold to Emil, and for the next few years they commuted to Peekskill, presumably alternating their visits.

The Grubbes' marriage, stormy and laced with scandal, ended in 1911. Emil's treatment of his Clara was not such as to reflect credit on his memory. Thirty years later, when he was 66, Emil proposed to an attractive woman of 34. For a wedding gift he offered to buy her an apartment building in which they would make their home, but, fortunately for the prospective bride, he started disciplining her while there was still time for her to change her mind. After they had inspected the property and were on the way to a real estate agent to close the deal, Emil informed his fiancée that they would live in the basement apartment so that all the others could be rented and that it must be clearly understood that no member of her family was ever to visit her or to be entertained in the new home.

Clara had had no such warning, however, and there is little likelihood that twelve years of married life in her new Chicago home brought much of warmth or love into her life. That she misbehaved flagrantly is established amply by reports of the private detectives her husband employed, court records, clippings from Chicago newspapers of February 13 and 14, 1911, and a postcard portrait of the tall young concert singer in whose company she sought the satisfactions denied her by her husband.

Half a century later, the most noteworthy feature of this collection is not the story it tells of a pitifully shabby illicit romance, but rather the picture it draws of the sadistic vengeance of the wronged husband, who carefully preserved the record of his wife's disgrace and included it among papers designated for use by his biographer.

At the police station, after he had run her to earth, Clara told Emil that she was wearing only a kimono under her long coat and pled for permission to return home for more clothing or to have some sent to her. According to the police report, Emil refused both requests; he gave her $5.00 and advised her to go to her sister's home in Evanston, twelve miles away and in the month of February.

Approximately a month later, after pleading in court that his income was a paltry $5.00 a day, Emil was granted a divorce and Clara was awarded $150 in lieu of alimony. Against this courtroom fiction is arrayed such evidence as Emil's purchase of an electric automobile at a time when only the rich could afford them and a growing accumulation of real estate, as well as his own statements about the phenomenal earnings of his various offices.

Five

The Man of Letters

In 1949, Emil paid the Bruce Publishing Co. of St. Paul, Minnesota, $2,000 to publish and distribute his book, *X-Ray Treatment: Its Origin, Birth, and Early History*, with 153 pages, 15 chapters, and 51 illustrations. By April, 1952, 550 volumes had been disposed of by sale or gifts; publishing costs amounted to approximately $2,600, income from sales was about $1,100, and the author's net monetary investment amounted to approximately $1,500. To this must be added the expenditure of effort by himself and by the devoted friend who typed manuscript and corrected proof, but for Emil these investments of money and effort were well repaid by the satisfaction of authorship.

"The book" lists a total of ninety of Emil's publications, beginning with an 1895 dissertation on distilled water, written for the Hahnemann medical school publication, *The Pulse*, at the time when Emil was at once student and instructor in the chemistry department. This publication, by the way, refutes Emil's contention, made later in life, that it was lack of access to medical journals which prevented his prompt publication of his January, 1896 treatment of Mrs. Lee and Mr. Carr. Among the other publications listed in the book, eighteen are merely routine reports in another Hahnemann publication, *The Clinique*, of clinical sessions at that institution; in the case of the remainder, duplication is so frequent (some papers appearing as many as five times in various places) that the list shrinks to approximately forty. I have been able to lay my hands on thirty-three and, having done so, have imposed on myself the duty of reading through the lot.

Most, but not all, appeared in off-beat journals, and I found them tediously dull, save for an occasional hilarious flash of the ridiculous. Here is an uninhibited cultist writing for an audience of fellow cultists and doing so at a time when discriminating editorial policy and responsible authorship had become common-place in American medicine of the "regular" variety.

The thirty-three articles are abstracted below and five of them (Nos. 2, 5, 19, 25, and 31) are reproduced in Appendix I.

1. "The Principles of Chemical Philosophy," *The Pulse*, December, 1896, and January, 1897. An exposition of general chemistry at the high school level.

2. "The Value of a Static Machine to the General Practitioner," *The Alkaloidal Clinic*, April, 1901. Reproduced in full in Appendix I.

3. "The So-called Inaccuracies and Fallacies of the X-Rays," *American Electro-Therapeutic and X-Ray Era*, 1901. A puff for the Illinois X-Ray and Electro-Therapeutic Laboratory.

In this article appears the illustration of an inverted knee, mentioned in Chapter IV, without text reference of any sort. It appeared again in a seven-page advertising booklet Emil wrote for Western Surgical Instrument House, 647 W. 59th Street, Chicago, with the legend, "Showing Buck-Shot in Arm." Only those who write little escape the embarrassment of occasionally letting inverted illustrations and erroneous legends escape them when reading proof. But to have the identical accident happen twice is unusual and indicative I believe, of carelessness or overwork, or perhaps both.

4. "X-Ray Tubes," *American X-Ray Journal*, 1901, and in four other places, including another Birtman Company catalogue. This oft-repeated paper has led the authors of some of the sketches on Grubbe to state that he was a manufacturer of X-ray tubes and that the ones he sent to the Smithsonian were of his own making. Actually he has said flatly that he did no commercial manufacturing. The tubes presented to Smithsonian bear the markings of well-known commercial manufacturers.

5. "X-Rays in the Treatment of Cancer and Other Malignant Diseases," *The Medical Record*, November 1, 1902 (and in five other places during the years 1902–3). Emil's earliest exposition of his employment of X-rays as a necrotizing agent to "burn out" even deep-seated cancers was written at a time when the disastrous sequelae of such procedures had not yet been suspected, much less demonstrated. Reproduced in Appendix I.

6. "Results and Technique in Treating Epithelioma with X-

Rays," Read before the American Roentgen Ray Society in Chicago, December 10, 1902. Published in the *Journal of Advance Therapeutics* and in nine other places. Many words but little substance about the relationship between the vacuum within X-ray tube and the condition that is to be treated. A continuous dermatitis was said to be required for cure, a fact which even patients had come to recognize. When lesions thought to be lupus or carcinoma failed to respond, the diagnosis must have been in error.

7. "Modern Uses of X-Rays," *Our Day*, February, 1903. An exposition for non-physicians in a non-medical publication.

8. "Electricity in Gynecology," *The Surgical Clinics*, April, 1903. In many ways, an earlier edition of No. 20 (dated 1912). It deals only slightly with X-rays, being largely concerned with the use of galvanism, faradism, and static "surging" for the treatment of such conditions as amenorrhea, dysmenorrhea, fibroids, and pelvic inflammatory disease, including gonorrhea, as well as for prolapse, subinvolution, version flexion, and underdevelopment of the uterus.

9. "General Electro-Therapeutic and X-Ray Clinic," by Grubbe, Laura Brown, and Cecilia P. Gallogly, in *American Electro-Therapeutic and X-Ray Era*, June, 1903. This is one of eighteen similar reports on teaching clinics at Hahnemann Hospital.

10. "High Frequency Electric Currents in Medicine," *American Electro-Therapeutic and X-Ray Era*, December, 1903; *Western Electrician and Medical Brief*, 1904; and *The Journal of Treatment*, July, 1904. Begins with a high school type of discussion of electric currents before proceeding to a list of the many ills which respond to the clinical application of high-frequency electricity. Such treatment is alleged to increase blood pressure, oxygenate the blood, bring urea-uric acid ratio into balance, increase body heat, produce anesthesia, and cure eczema, acne, psoriasis, carcinoma, fissured ulcers, catarrhal mucous membranes, neuralgia, sciatica, gout, tuberculosis, obesity, diabetes, and such cases of lupus as may be resistant to X-ray treatment.

11. "X-Rays in the Treatment of Pulmonary Tuberculosis," read at American Roentgen Ray Society Meeting, October, 1904, and published in the *Alkaloidal Clinic*, the *Archives of Electro-Therapy and Radiology*, *The Clinique*, and *Physical Therapy*. Of

fifty-four patients, twenty were cured, sixteen improved, twelve discontinued the treatment, and six died. While it is not claimed that radiation is specific for the disease, still it does destroy tubercle bacilli, control hemorrhage and pain, and in general stimulate the patient. Undoubtedly part of the favorable response must be credited to the ozone produced about the wires leading to the X-ray tube.

12. "X-Ray Tubes," An Emil H. Grubbe contribution to the Birtman catalogue for the year 1904.

13. "Roentgen Rays and Radioactive Substances as Therapeutic Agents," presented to International Electric Congress, St. Louis, 1904, and published as an advance copy of Section H. Appeared also October 6, 1906, in *Scientific American*, Supplement 1605. That Emil should have confused fluoroscence with radioactivity in the year 1904 is not surprising, but whereas most others soon came to recognize the error of that concept, Emil carried the conviction to his grave. In the treatment here described, a solution of strontium salicylate in normal salt solution was injected into or around deep neoplasms, or crystals of the substance were scattered over the surface of superficial ones. X-rays were then applied, and the results were far superior to those obtained from X-rays alone. In addition to local reaction, there was a sedative and anodyne effect and a "tonic" stimulation of nutritive processes.

14. "Contribution to Symposium on Roentgen Rays in Skin Diseases," *American Journal of Dermatology*, April, 1907. Among the thirty contributors, some were very fast company indeed for Emil, including such physicians as Piffard of New York, Soiland of Los Angeles, Sjorgren of Stockholm, Boggs of Pittsburgh, and Leonard of Philadelphia. Even though he was more restrained than usual, Emil's conclusions contrasted sharply with those of Piffard. Emil said, in part: "X-Rays have been found to be of value either as a primary or adjunct measure in the treatment of nearly every local skin disease in the catalogue . . . there are practically no contra indications for their use." Piffard had set the tone of the symposium in the closing paragraph of his brief introductory talk in which he said "The limit of radio mania has, I think, been reached by a recent writer from whom I quote the following: 'It [X-ray] may be considered a specific in all forms of acne, lupus, eczema, psoriasis, pruritus, tinea, and sycosis, mycosisfungoides,

senile keratoses, venereal condylomata, and hyperidrosis.' I can add however, without regret, that the writer of this sentence is one who is not specially known in dermatological circles."

15. "X-Ray Diagnosis of Calculi in the Urinary System," *The Clinique*, September, 1908. A reasonable presentation for the days before Potter's invention of the moving grid and the introduction of duplitized films and double intensifying screens. It contains, however, the preposterous suggestion that X-ray plates must be developed in solutions so weak that processing requires up to an hour. One is tempted to quip that this is a foible of a devout homeopath.

16. "The X-Ray Treatment of Acne," *American Journal of Physiologic Therapeutics*, May, 1910. Unfortunately, Emil was not alone among Chicago physicians of the period in believing that there was "not one case of undesirable effect." Many of them and their patients lived to regret the four to eight weeks of treatment administered to acute lesions and the eight to ten for those that were chronic. This paper appeared in several other places.

17. "Value of X-Ray in Fractures," *The Clinique*, September, 1910, and three years later in *Medical Brief*. An undistinguished, unillustrated treatment of a commonplace subject. The best that can be said of it is that it advises against using the fluoroscope for diagnosing or manipulating fractures.

18. "The Crime against Physical Therapeutics," A polemic address delivered in 1912 by Emil, as President of the National Physical Therapeutics Society, and published that year and the next in the *Journal of the American Institute of Homeopathy*, *Physical Therapeutics*, and *Medical Brief*. Recent recasting of medical school curricula had omitted this specialty to the disadvantage of practitioners, patients, and particularly of medical students who, having paid tuition for complete instruction, were now denied it. Every phase of medicine should be taught in every medical school.

19. "Treatment of Dysmenorrhea with Faradic Electricity," *The Clinique*, January, 1912, reproduced in Appendix I: Dysmenorrhea can be cured by "exercising the uterine muscle, and this is most easily done by rhythmic stimulation produced by electricity. When patency of the cervix permits, a bipolar electrode is introduced into the uterine cavity. In cases where this is not possible, one

Emil H. Grubbe

electrode in the vagina makes contact with the cervix and the other lies in the rectum."

20. "A List of Diseases in Which X-Ray Treatment Is of Value," *The Clinique*, October, 1912, and *Medical Brief*, September 13, 1912. Included are acne, alopecia areata, carbuncle, carcinoma, chronic ulcers, eczema, epithelioma, elephantiasis, favus, goiter, Hodgkin's disease, hypertrichosis, hyperidrosis, keloid, senile keratosis, leukemia, naevus, osteosarcoma, pruritus ani et vulvae, psoriasis, rodent ulcer, recurrent growths, sycosis, sarcoma, trachoma, tuberculosis of skin glands, bones, joints, lungs, and larynx, tubercular sinuses and fistulae, and varicose veins.

21. "X-Rays in the Diagnosis of Diseases of Bones and Joints," *Hahnemann Monthly*, November, 1913; *Journal of the American Institute of Homeopathy*, April, 1914; and *Medical Brief*, June, 1914. When one attempts to discuss tuberculosis, syphilis, and necrosis of bone, rickets, scurvy, periostitis, arthritis, gout, rheumatoid arthritis, bone cysts, deformities, osteosarcoma, chondroma, osteoma, and osteomyelitis without recourse to pathology or even to reproduced radiographs, he can expect to wind up with a miserable mess. This article includes neither illustrations nor descriptions of tissue.

22. "The X-Ray Treatment of Skin Cancer," *American Journal of Clinical Medicine*, December, 1913; and *Medical Brief*, August, 1914. A precursor to No. 25, which has been reproduced in full.

23. "X-Rays and Radioactive Chemicals in the Treatment of Gynecological Conditions," *Medical Record*, July 18, 1914; and *Medical Brief*, November, 1914. Now Emil uses the term radioactive in its proper sense and is talking about radium. He uses radium but prefers X-rays in spite of the fact that they include alpha and beta rays which must be filtered out with aluminum. Small ports (he calls them diaphragms), as is well known, concentrate X-rays, he says, as making for sharper images in diagnosis and reduced skin doses in therapy!

24. "X-Ray Treatment of Fibroid Tumor," *The Clinique*, probably in March, 1915. Cured by radiation-induced menopause. Modern tubes (the hot-cathode variety is meant, perhaps) simplify the work of the therapist.

25. "One Hundred and Thirty-Nine Cases of Skin Cancer Cured by X-Rays," appeared in *Interstate Medical Journal*, Oc-

56

tober, 1916, Supplement on Roentgenology, as well as in *The Clinique* and *The Journal of Advance Therapeutics*, and as an address to the Illinois Homeopathic Medical Association. In my opinion this is Emil's best writing and is on a subject in which he had indeed become recognized as having experience and competence. However, despite the fact that by this time much information had become available as to the physical nature of X-rays, Emil still insisted in this article, as he would continue to insist repeatedly and erroneously until his death, that X-rays were made up of alpha, beta, and gamma components. Reproduced in Appendix I.

26. "Electrical Treatment of Infantile Paralysis," *Illinois Medical Journal*, December 1917. Not specific for the disease but far and away the best means of preventing deformities. Treatment cannot be started until soreness has left the muscles, but must not be delayed until atrophy has occurred. Decisions as to timing and other details require an expert. In all adults use static electricity, adjusting contraction rate for the part being treated, and keeping current just barely strong enough to incite contractions. In children, use galvanic current unless muscle damage is so severe that static alone will serve.

27. "X-Ray Therapy in Uterine Cancer," *Interstate Medical Journal*, 1917. The most restrained of Emil's cancer-therapy papers, suggesting that with the passage of time, the utter futility of treating deep-seated neoplasm with the quality of radiation that served so well in superficial neoplasms had begun to dawn on him. In the following year there was to come from postwar Germany the great technical breakthrough that enabled radiologists to operate their tubes at double the previous voltage, thus making the irradiation of pelvic neoplasm a scientific fact rather than the laying on of hands which it had been before that time.

28. "Electrolysis in the Removal of Superfluous Hair," *American Journal of Dermatology and Genito-Urinary Disease*, 1910. X-rays and other agents may be employed but electrolysis is safest and best. Instruments and technique are described.

29. "X-Ray Treatment of Skin Cancer," *American Journal of Clinical Medicine*, December, 1918. To the cases previously published four more are added.

30. "Who Was the First To Make Use of the Therapeutic

Qualities of the X-Ray?" *The Radiological Review*, August, 1933, Vol. XXII, pp. 184–87. This and the simultaneously published No. 31 are the fruits of reading at Crerar Library in preparation for the Congress of Radiology to be held in Chicago. Presumably it was No. 31 that Emil had in mind when he closed No. 30 with the statement, "In another paper which will appear shortly I shall give a detailed, step-by-step, historical version of all the scientific work which preceded the discovery of the X-rays. I shall also give detailed, historical accounts of the records of all those for whom credit for priority in the therapeutic use of the X-rays have been made [*sic*].

"In challenging the validity of the claims made for others I make use of the statements, when obtainable, of the individuals involved. I also use the calendar in order to properly place in chronological order the work for which each should receive credit.

"Considered from a purely historical standpoint, I promise that that paper will be one of the most momentous in X-Ray literature."

31. "Priority in the Therapeutic Use of X-Rays," *Radiology*, August, 1933, Vol. XXI, pp. 156–62. Reproduced in Appendix I.

32. "X-Ray Treatment: Its Introduction to Medicine," *Journal of the American Institute of Homeopathy*, Vol. XXXIX, No. 12, 1946, pp. 419–22. A rehash of 30 and 31.

33. *X-Ray Treatment: Its Origin, Birth, and Early History*, St. Paul and Minneapolis: The Bruce Publishing Co., 1949, 153 pp. This is "the book."

Starting with No. 30 in 1933 and culminating with No. 33 in 1949 these four publications appeared to Emil to nail down his claim to medical immortality. All four tell the same story in varying detail, and if anyone has questioned the validity of the claims, I have found no published record of such questioning. On the contrary, writers in newspapers, magazines, and even medical journals, believing Emil's own accounts of his activities as gospel, usually took off from there with embellished rewrites. After the ball had been batted back and forth a few times Emil began quoting this parroting of his own words as new source material buttressing his claims.

Emil declared himself to be a member of the following twenty societies:

1. Charter member of the Roentgen Society of the United States, which eventually became the American Roentgen Ray Society.

2. Founder of the Chicago Electro-Medical Society, which later became the Chicago Roentgen Society.

3. Founder of the Western Radiological Society, which later became the Radiological Society of North America.

4. Confrère of the International Electrical Congress, Paris, 1900.

5. Delegate to the International Electrical Congress, St. Louis, 1904.

6. American Congress of Physical Therapy, 1938.

7. Diplomate, American Board of Radiology, 1937.

8. Fellow, American College of Physicians, 1920.

9. Associate Fellow, American Medical Association.

10. National Society of Physical Therapeutics.

11. Association of American Physicians.

12. National Academy of Science.

13. American Association for Cancer Research.

14. Illinois Medical Society.

15. Chicago Medical Society.

16. American Association for the Advancement of Science.

17. Association of Approved Radiologists.

18. The Press Club of Chicago.

19. The North Shore Philatelic Society.

20. The Chicago Electro-Medical Society.

I have not checked all these claims, but where I have checked they have been confirmed, except in two important instances, namely, numbers 1 and 12. The office of the home secretary of the National Academy of Sciences assures me that Emil was not a member. Possibly he confused this important national organization with the Illinois State Academy of Science, for which there is among his papers a bill for dues for the years 1932–34.

As to charter membership in the American Roentgen Ray Society (claim 1), the records of that society refute the claim and indicate that even Emil's ordinary membership was a brief and stormy affair.

Organized in St. Louis on March 26, 1900, as the Roentgen Ray Society of the United States, the organization met for the first time

Emil H. Grubbe

December 13 and 14, 1900, in New York City. Invitations had been mailed and were published in the *American X-Ray Journal* of St. Louis, offering charter membership on payment of $5.00, but Emil failed to take advantage of the offer, and by the time the published transactions began to list the names of members, he was listed as an ordinary rather than a charter member.

At the New York meeting the name was changed to the Roentgen Society of America. At the second meeting, in Buffalo in 1901, Emil spoke on "The X-Ray Tubes" and was listed as a member. In 1902, the meeting was in Chicago, the name had been changed again, to the present title, the American Roentgen Ray Society, and Emil spoke on "Results and Technique in Treating Epithelioma with X-Rays." Now, for the first time, there were published lists distinguishing between charter members and regular members, Emil being listed among the latter. The fourth meeting was in Philadelphia in 1903, and Emil discussed a paper by others, but gave none of his own, but he was back on the program for the fifth meeting in St. Louis in 1904.

The treasurer's records for the society, which begin with the year 1902, show that Emil was elected to membership in December, 1901, paying the dues (at that time $5.00 per year) for the years 1901, 1902, 1903, and 1905, but not for 1904, 1906, or 1907, at which time his membership was suspended, presumably in connection with internal society strife which the late Edward H. Skinner has described in a monograph on the history of the society, published in connection with its fiftieth anniversary meeting in St. Louis in 1950.[1] Dr. Skinner says:

> In March 1900 a small group of Mid-Western physicians met at the offices of the American X-Ray Journal in St. Louis, Missouri, to organize the Roentgen Ray Society of the United States. Dr. Heber Robarts of St. Louis had established the American Roentgen Ray Society in 1897 and continued as editor through 1902. In organizing the Roentgen Society of the United States, Dr. Robarts was elected the first chairman and Dr. Rudis-Jicinsky of Cedar Rapids, Iowa, was elected secretary. No membership list of

---

[1] *The American Roentgen Ray Society 1900–1950* (Springfield, Ill.: Charles C Thomas, 1950). Limited edition.

this group has been located, but the committee listings for the first annual meeting which was held at the Grand Central Palace in New York City on December 14–15, 1900, shows eighteen names. It is reported that there were 150 persons attending this meeting, including exhibitors, and that papers were scheduled on the program.

The first published listing of members is found in the transactions of the third annual meeting, which was held in Chicago, Illinois, in December, 1902. This list shows 64 charter members and a total membership of 221. The first program which has been located is that of the second annual meeting at Buffalo, New York, in 1901, September 10–11. Dr. Robarts reported that 105 members attended and paid dues at this meeting.

These first two meetings must have been chaotic affairs. The documentary evidence, mostly within the columns of the issues of the American X-Ray Journal seems to show that a fringe of electro-therapists (some of whom must have been homeopaths like Emil) attempted to either control or sabotage this poorly organized society, much to the embarrassment of Dr. Robarts. They attempted to euchre the editor out of his journal and finally succeeded in about two years.

The name of the society was changed in 1901 to "the Roentgen Society of America" because Canadian physicians were desirable members. In the transactions of the third annual meeting, which was held in Chicago, Illinois, in 1902, the constitution and bylaws were changed to the American Roentgen Ray Society.

About fifty new members were added at the third annual meeting in Chicago in 1902, and many of them became familiar figures in the society, fighting for a clean ethical society and later making names in radiology. Eight of these new members were elected to the presidency of the society in due course.

The early days of the society must have been quite trying, and in many respects even disastrous to Dr. Robarts. Fortunately or otherwise, almost none of those identified with the first wrangling meeting remained among the membership for more than three years. None of the Eastern roentgenologists, who were already contributing brilliantly to the new specialty, even attended the first meeting. Later however, they did attend the meetings and became invaluable members. . . .

Within two years, however, the society was rescued from its despoilers and detracters, and the improvement and progress has been constant ever since.

Strife was not restricted to contacts between the cultists and regular physicians, however, and, as sometimes happens in civil war, brother fought brother even more savagely than he had reacted to outsiders.

Emil probably felt a proprietary interest in the Chicago Electro-Medical Society (No. 20), because its organizational meeting in June, 1901, had been held on home grounds in the Champlain Building, with his partners Gilman and Street among its officers. He was a discussant at its first meeting, held in the Palmer House in July of that year. Another member was Dr. H. P. Pratt. It soon developed that one society was not large enough to contain both Emil and H. P., each of whom maintained that he, and he alone, was first to have employed X-rays therapeutically. After considerable bitter in-fighting the society was dissolved, only to have Pratt revive it with a membership purged of the deluded Grubbe disciples and staffed with Pratt adherents, who promptly went on record with a resolution awarding Pratt his coveted patent of originality. The Grubbe faction responded by re-establishing their version of the society, and eventually obtained a court order declaring them to be the true and sole owners of the Chicago Electro-Medical Society.

As to the Press Club of Chicago, to which he was elected in 1913, Emil has left little for his biographer. He has, however, preserved without comment several dozen cartoons ca.1905 by Ralph Wilder and ca.1908 by Rankin, featuring a "Mister Grubbe." Wilder's Grubbe was a pompous blowhard and Rankin's a timid, frustrated little fellow. One wonders, but at this late date in vain, whether the cartoonists were among members of the press who somewhat later were to rub shoulders with Emil at the Press Club and whether by any chance he thought himself to be, or was in fact, the subject of their lampooning.

In the winter of 1948–49 Emil became interested in newspaper accounts of the gift to the John Crerar Library of books and correspondence of Dr. Clifford G. Grulee, the well-known pediatrician, and made several penciled notes, some of which read as follows:

Miss Salmonsen: [2] I have to move—may have to leave town. I want to give The Crerar Library my scientific and medical books, many of them ancient especially in the X-ray and electrical fields, (almost similar to Dr. Clifford Grulee's collection which he gave your library recently). My hobby has been philosophy and so, I have a large number of philosophical books to give you if your library wants them. If you don't want them I will give them to the Chicago Public Library. Let me hear from you.

Another note to himself:

You called on Henkle [3] and Salmonsen 1/31/49 and told them you wanted newspaper publicity credits from both Crerar and Newberry. I think I am entitled to a separate personal credit from the Newberry Library though as I gave them the books directly.

Another note reads:

Give all books to Crerar—they will help themselves to whatever they want and then will give the rest to Newberry Library. (Ask Salmonsen to see that you get credit from both libraries.)

And still another note:

I think I should get a little newspaper publicity when I give more than a thousand books to two libraries. Remember the publicity you gave Dr. Grulee was the cause of my giving my books to Crerar and Newberry libraries. So, if you give me publicity perhaps you will get other donations.

Mr. Henkle and Miss Salmonsen visited Dr. Grubbe and on January 11, 1949, Mr. Henkle wrote, referring to the visit, asking permission to select from the material and expressing interest in correspondence files which had not been shown to him and in a supposedly very valuable stamp collection which had been shown but not offered to the library.

On page 213 of the April, 1949, number of the *Illinois Medical Journal* there appeared the following note entitled, "Private Library Donated to Crerar Library."

---

[2] Miss Ella M. Salmonsen, medical librarian, the John Crerar Library.

[3] Mr. Herman Henkle, librarian of the John Crerar Library.

Emil H. Grubbe

Dr. Emil H. Grubbe, pioneer in X-ray therapy, has given his private library to the John Crerar Library according to an announcement just issued by Herman H. Henkle, the librarian. The gift makes important additions to the research collection of the library in the fields of X-ray, X-ray therapy, and related technical subjects. The collection given by Dr. Grubbe numbers about 1,000 volumes.

As an experimentor and manufacturer of X-ray apparatus, Dr. Grubbe first suffered X-ray burns more than fifty years ago. On January 27, 1896, he exhibited the detrimental effects produced by over-exposure to X-rays to a group of physicians in Chicago. Acting on the suggestion that the new X-rays might have value in the treatment of diseased tissues, Dr. Grubbe applied X-rays to a number of patients. These experiments marked the beginning of X-ray therapy. Five early X-ray tubes used by Dr. Grubbe, original documents, letters, records, and other evidence pertaining to Dr. Grubbe's claim to priority as the originator of X-ray therapy are on deposit with the Smithsonian Institution, United States National Museum in Washington, D.C.

In Dr. Benjamin H. Orndoff's obituary of Dr. Grubbe, published in *Radiology*, Vol. LXXVII, September, 1960, pp. 473–74 (reproduced in Appendix II), the following statement appears "Some ten years earlier, he had made a gift to the John Crerar Library, Chicago, of his private library consisting of about a thousand volumes on roentgenography, roentgen therapy, and related technical subjects."

On April 30, 1952, Mr. Herman H. Henkle sent to Dr. Grubbe one of the formal certificates issued by the directors of the Library, acknowledging the receipt of a copy of *X-Ray Treatment, Its Origin, Birth, and Early History*, and thanking the author for the gift. No other acknowledgment was found among Emil's papers.

From available evidence the facts appear to me to be about as follows: Mr. Henkle and Miss Salmonsen went to Emil's place with high hopes but found little of value among his books. They still hoped however, that with a little prodding, he could be induced to include the stamp collection in the gift, and assumed that his own appraisal of its great importance and value was correct. In the Grulee collection, to which reference had been made by Emil, one of the most important parts had been correspondence files. Mr. Henkle assumed that Emil had similar files though he had not seen them at the time of the visit.

Eventually approximately fifty books were transferred to Crerar and the stamp collection, actually of relatively small monetary value, was given to the University of Chicago. The "correspondence files," as the biographer knows to his sorrow, consisted merely of random, largely undated notes and clippings, and here and there actual letters. Inadequate as they are, they have been far better than nothing for filling out certain portions of this biography, but certainly they were not the sort of material that Mr. Henkle had in mind.

Presumably most of the "books" were the leaflets, magazines, and pamphlets of an antireligious nature which made up so large a part of the scores of pounds of material transferred to the university after Emil's death.

How shall we account for the *Illinois Medical Journal* article which refers to "an announcement just issued by Herman H. Henkle" and for Dr. Orndoff's reference to the Crerar gift? I believe that the latter stemmed from the former, and that the former was from copy prepared by Emil himself and transmitted to the *Journal* without previous consultation with the Crerar authorities. I am convinced that Emil's reading was largely of newspapers, medical journals, and his antireligious tracts, and that the several weeks of reading at Crerar in preparation for the 1933 and 1949 publications was something rather unusual for him.

Six

RADIATION INJURIES

In view of the multitude of stories told by Emil and others about his radiation injuries and the surgery performed on them, it is surprising how little real information exists. In the one instance in which he has been specific there is reason to believe that his memory played him false. I refer to his statement relative to alleged bone marrow involvement. Emil says:

> I went to Johns Hopkins University at Baltimore, Maryland, on (Tuesday) February 15, 1896, to consult Dr. William Osler about my radiation troubles. He was in Montreal, Canada, and would be there for a week, so I had to go to Canada to see him. After he examined me, he sent me back to Johns Hopkins to have my blood tested by Dr. William H. Welch. Dr. Welch reported that I had a bad case of aplastic anemia. Both Dr. Osler and Dr. Welch agreed that my condition was serious and that I might die within six months.

It was Emil's belief that he did, in fact, suffer from anemia but that a daily consumption of fresh beef blood and wine enabled him to combat it and outlive the two Baltimore physicians who had predicted his early demise. Emil says he frequently took a gallon jug of red wine to the stockyards, armed with a pass to the skinning room issued by his former neighbor and newspaper patron, Gustaf Swift. He bribed the skinners with half of the wine and in return received a half-gallon of freshly drawn blood to mix with the remaining wine. Swift, he says, "presently got the idea" and began offering such mixtures commercially to druggists.

Two facts make me skeptical of this story.

1. The subject of radiation injuries was studied and reported on by workers at Johns Hopkins during the early years of radiology, and when I was unable to find among the reported cases any that

66

seemed to be Emil's, I sought the assistance of friends at the university. Through them, librarians and members of the Department of the History of Medicine at Hopkins have searched back to the first hospital admission but find no record whatever of Emil's purported visit. All concerned consider it would have been out of character for either Osler or Welch to fail to record the fact if he actually did see Emil as a patient, but of course that possibility exists.

2. Blood-and-wine mixtures were among the offerings in druggist's advertisements at least as early as 1895, the year before Emil had even heard of X-rays, much less suffered from exposure to them.

That the severe dermatitis which developed toward the end of January, 1896, involved the dorsal surface of Emil's left hand is not surprising, because that was precisely the lesion suffered by many other early X-ray workers. It was commonplace then, and for many years later, to use the left hand as a test object for determining whether X-rays were being produced in the desired amount. The operator regularly held a small hooded fluoroscope in his right hand and interposed the left between tube and fluoroscopic screen, with the dorsum toward the tube; with the unfiltered, low-voltage radiation then in use, the dorsum received vastly more radiation than the palm. Furthermore, such testing would have been particularly frequent and prolonged when an operator was building or modifying X-ray tubes rather than merely using them clinically.

No information is available as to the time lapse between desquamation (loss of skin) and the healing of the first burn, but we are told that after healing the new skin was hairless, pigmented, and inelastic so that it abraded on slight trauma. Hyperesthesia and keratoses came later, and eventually atrophy of the skin of the fingers and of the other hand.

A penciled copy of "Dr. Wilson's report" dated June 24, 1920, records the fact that an excised ulcer (presumably from a finger of the left hand) shows destruction of epithelium and presence of abnormal round cells and connective tissue, but no malignancy; six months later more excised tissue looked about the same as the earlier specimen.

During a snowstorm at 6:20 P.M. on Thursday, March 7, 1929, Emil, then 54 years old, was struck by a hit-and-run driver as he was crossing Montrose and Clarendon avenues on Chicago's North Side. Unconscious at first and with his left hand mangled, he was taken to Lakeview Hospital where he remained for six days, returning April 2 for amputation of the left forearm at the wrist. The pre-existing radiation dermatitis presumably made it unwise to attempt to save the hand after it had been damaged. The right hand remained usable, however, and one who knew him in 1930 says that except for the amputation there was at that time little outward evidence of radiation damage.

Twelve years after the amputation an engineer friend sent Emil a description of an ingenious, battery-operated prosthesis which he proposed to make for him. A sketch accompanied the description. Among Emil's clippings there is one dealing with similar devices used to operate the jaws and claws of the costumes worn by actors in horror movies. But nothing came of the project.

Emil underwent partial resections of the upper lip in late 1929 and again in early 1930; in December, 1931, a surgeon curetted and cauterized nine epitheliomatous lesions from undesignated sites. In the following May the patient himself applied an electrical cautery to fifteen epitheliomatous lesions, in addition to a recurrence on his upper lip, and the years that followed saw numerous additional resections and amputations. By 1951, the resulting disfigurement made it necessary for Emil to move from the rented quarters he had been occupying because his landlord did not care to have handicapped or disabled tenants.

With this and several other instances of unsympathetic or downright cruel public reaction to his increasing disfigurement, he began to infer similar reactions where none existed and to avoid contacts with strangers. On the few occasions when he did appear in public he wore a glove on what remained of his right hand and an improvised adhesive-plaster prosthesis to cover the defect in his lip.

Notoriously short-tempered and opinionated during most of his adult life, his temper worsened with increasing infirmity, as might be expected; although doctors, nurses, and friends never failed to be moved to pity by his condition and to exert themselves mightily on his behalf, they found it difficult to take his browbeating with equanimity. One of his closest friends sometimes was able to convert a snarl to a grin by calling him to his face, "Old Meany." During one particularly painful period he intimated that he was contemplating suicide, but he was easily talked out of the idea.

Emil held pathologists in low esteem and did not hesitate to say so. Usually, he said, the things they called cancers were not cancers at all, and no one, he asserted, had ever heard of a radiation victim dying of metastases. He believed that if, like him, they were submitted to prompt and repeated excisions, they would be spared the consequences of absorbing toxins from tissue necrotized by X-rays. In the absence of such amputations, however, gangrene occurred and absorption from it caused death. As so frequently is the case, the pathologists had the last word; Emil's death certificate described multiple squamous cell carcinomas with regional metastases, plus terminal bronchopneumonia.

Seven

TRAVELS

Innumerable news stories and works of fiction testify to society's vulnerability to dissemblance, and it is a commonplace observation that except in small villages women are accepted as wives, bank accounts as the fruits of legitimate effort, and medical degrees and a host of other credentials as genuine, merely because a man represents them to be so. A plausible dissembler gets away with it until a break of luck leads someone to test one of his spurious claims, but once his bubble has been pricked, he faces skepticism even when he speaks the truth. Dr. Orndoff had no reason to doubt Grubbe's own accounts of his travels and the accounts of others and was reporting what he assumed to be fact when in the obituary he referred to "abundant home support for higher education and for travel and for research."

Reminded of the hopeless discrepancies between Emil's account of platinum in Idaho and the records of our federal government and of the government of Idaho, I was prepared from the first to suspect his reports of world-wide travel; having read what he says, I have become more, rather than less, skeptical. Parental resources were meager rather than abundant; at least until 1895 the only travels of record had been the free canal boat ride of a few dozen miles and such trips (to "Mexico, Canada, British Columbia and . . . the western . . . United States") as were undertaken during vacation periods for the assayer, Mr. Small.

Later in life Emil certainly had the means and no doubt could have found the leisure for any sort of travel that suited his whim, and perhaps he did do such traveling in the years shortly before World War I, when money was no longer lacking and passports were not yet required. His claims, however, are of extensive travels made long before that period. Among the myriad of penciled notes that have come to me there is one, obviously intended as a mem-

70

orandum to himself and characteristically undated, which reads:

> Add to *Who's Who* record: Physician, X-ray Specialist, Professor, Scientist, Explorer. Latter part of the last century and early part of this century explored all the diamond fields throughout the world, among them India, Borneo, in Africa, in South America (Brazil, British Guiana), also climbed and explored all the active volcanoes throughout the world. In 1902 was an eye-witness to the destruction of San Pierre by Mount Pelee, one of the greatest holocausts that ever occurred to mankind—40,000 human beings lost their lives in the eruption of this volcano.

Approximately eight years before his death, Emil started to write what he called an autobiography, and he has left for his biographer several dozen scraps of various sorts and sizes and including blue notepaper carrying the address of his former office at 130 North State Street, the backs of advertisements from drug houses, a 1953 notice to security holders of the Pacific Power & Light Co., a notice from his broker, and a 1954 advertisement of a stock market research company. One of his best friends and greatest admirers knew of the existence of these notes and had discussed them with Emil; she tells me that when she accused him of "drawing a long bow" his reply was not the explosion she expected, but, instead, a sheepish green. A small part of this material is reproduced so that the reader may see for himself the statements which lead to my almost complete skepticism.

> Page 2 of notebook. (Page 1 missing) b–hospital work.
> Chapter 7, teaching postgraduate school—
> a. Illinois School of Electro-Therapeutics
> b. Teaching in three other medical schools
> c. Doing X-ray work in other hospitals.
> Chapter 8—Electric Furnace
> a. Diamond manufacturing
> b. Coal, volcanoes
> Chapter 9—Exploring and Travels
> 1900-g-Paris. 1896-b-California—Mount Lassen
> 1896-c-Grand Canyon, Arizona
> 1911-j-Alaska, Siberia, British Columbia
> ?1915-u-Mexico, Central America
> ?1904-h-Martinique, Mount Pelee
> 1898-f-Brazil, British Guiana
> 1897-e-Africa-Congo-Boer Country
> 1920-o-Australia, New Zealand

Emil H. Grubbe

1912-k-India, China, Ceylon
1895-a-Colorado, Idaho
1914-m-Norway, Spitzbergen, North Pole
1913-l-Argentine, Awkland Islands, South Pole
1906-i-Lower California, Mexico
1896-d-British Colombia

In the summer of 1895 I was in business as assayer and refiner of fine metals. Among other things, I devised an electric furnace primarily for the purpose of refining platinum, but on reading about the theory of diamond formation in volcanoes, I also used this furnace for making small diamonds artificially. Because my body had been damaged by uncontrolled X-ray effect, I was advised to go to a warm climate, especially in the winter, and live out-of-doors several months each year. This led to my planning to go to most of the active volcanoes of at least the warmer parts of the globe in order to prove or disprove the theory of volcanic origins of diamonds. For a number of years these travels took me on exploring expeditions to many out-of-the-way places. Although these travels occurred years ago, I can at present write quite accurately about most of them because I don't have to trust my memory, having kept a diary, and when occasionally anything of importance occurred, I made extensive notes. Of course, through the years some of these notes have been lost but enough remain of each subject to allow me to give a fairly accurate account of the conditions which I encountered in each of the localities of which I write in this book. In general I might state that when I visited these out-of-the-way places I found no commercial developments or plant industries such as are found in most of these localities at the present time. Rubber, sugar, coffee, tobacco plantations and oil wells were nonexistent. The only products commercialized at that time were timber, roots, nuts, coal, metal and diamond mining, wild animals, their hides and tusks. Usually, the stillness of the jungle is appalling.

. . .

When you go into the jungle don't expect to find modern conveniences or comforts. In these tropical regions one has opportunity to view many handiworks of nature. The beauty of the landscape effects produced by proper placing of mountains, level land, vegetation, water and clouds, are often wonderful beyond description. . . . The reader must keep in mind that this region (territory) [unspeci-

72

fied] is only a few miles north of the equator and therefore the temperature is usually quite high.

Many species of ants in tropical countries are called "sewing ants" because these creatures fasten leaves together in such a manner that the finished product looks like the leaves were sewn together.

I realize that this book [*Philosophy of Irreligion*] is provocative. I intended it to be so. However, it is not my fault that it appears sensational to those who have not thought seriously about religious subjects. Morton Wheeler, a zoologist, who studied the social qualities of insects, especially ants, once said: "Through the studies of these social insects, man may come to understand his own organization better. Perhaps may even come to realize that he is not the only worthwhile living thing on the planet."

The Sangi Archipelago, south of the Philippines, has within its borders more volcanoes than any other area of similar size. There are literally thousands of them in the southeastern part of the world, between Australia and Asia. Practically the entire Netherland Indies, Borneo, and the New Guinea Islands are almost entirely volcanic. When the weather is very favorable and the clouds do not obscure the peaks, one of the greatest scenic views in the world can be obtained by cruising among the Netherland Indies. Yes, even volcanoes can be very magnificent.

.   .   .

I wanted to see and study volcanoes, at least those which were accessible and possibly those which showed unusual variation in structure. I wanted to see not only extinct volcanoes but also those which were active—in those days it was a dangerous and therefore serious matter to go so far away from home to the end of the earth, as it were. I must inform my readers that throughout the Orient, Sunday is not observed like it is in the western world. It is not a day of rest to the Oriental, but a workday just like any other day of the week. At the time I visited many of these places mentioned in this book (40 to 55 years ago) ordinary travelers were not permitted to enter. I, therefore, made it a point to get a United States government identification letter to someone in authority in the foreign country. In all my travels in foreign ports, I never have any fears of getting lost or of being helpless because I could not speak the language of the country I was going to enter. Invariably, in my planning for a visit to a given country, I would have some cards written in the language of that particular locality—one card telling who I was, another what I was there for, another asking for directions and advice. Usually the persons who read these cards would direct me to some-one to whom I could talk and I have seldom been misdi-rected or given the wrong information.

. . .

At the time I visited this [unspecified] region, little was known about the people or the products of the territory. These islands were not yet interesting to, or explored by white men—although there are many volcanoes in the world and a great many of them are periodically sending steam and smoke out of their peaks (cones), few of them are erupting at the present time.

Some of this material was used in a talk before the Chicago Philatelic Society, January 20, 1938, and appeared in the January, February, and (presumably) March numbers of that society's pub-lication, *C.P.S. News* (see appendix). Some more colorful excerpts follow.

India—a country less than one-third the size of the United States with a population of more than 360 million.
India—a country of contrasts, where live some of the richest, also many of the poorest human beings; the most highly educated, also the most ignorant; where the temper-ature is 125 degrees Fahrenheit in the shade in the valleys, and 10 degrees below zero near the top of Mt. Everest.
While waiting in the city of Nagpur for a guide whom I had engaged, I had some spare time and thought I might broaden my intellectual horizon by going into a second-hand bookshop on the opposite side of the street. Well, I picked up a large volume in the Nagpur bookshop. It was written in a language which I could not read, but neverthe-less I was exceedingly interested. The reason was that many pages of that book were filled with postally used Indian stamps, mostly of the early Feudal States issues. I asked the price of the book. It was one rupee (about 34 cents in our money). I paid my one rupee and had the storekeeper tie a string around the book, then I rushed out of the store across the street to my hotel. In crossing the street, I was in a daze at my stamp find and ran right into the rear end of a big elephant. I lost my balance and in trying to steady myself I again stumbled into the elephant, who resented my trying to push him off the street, by politely kicking me into the gutter where I landed on the summer's accumula-

tion of rubbish. My precious book of stamps was thrown some fifteen feet away, but fortunately, all the stamps in it had been pasted on the pages with starch and so I lost none of them.

At this point I anticipate something. I know all of you have a question which you would like to have me answer. Here is the answer: Yes, this one rupee purchase was a good buy. When I arrived at home and consulted the catalogue the stamps in this secondhand book were valued at $205.00.

Borneo—the home of the chimpanzee (the man ape), also the home of wild men and wilder women; where human beings live in huts built in the tops of trees: where a girl, when asked for her hand in marriage says "yes" to her prospective husband *only* when he presents her with the head of one of his rivals.

Africa—where Zulus, Kaffirs, Hottentots, Pygmies, and other colored races do all the work and the white man takes all the gravy—all the profits.

Among the palpable flaws in this preposterous tale are the following:

1. Manufacture of synthetic diamonds requires great pressure, in addition to high temperatures, and it is inconceivable that in that little room in Grant's stationery store there were facilities for producing those pressures and temperatures some decades before well-equipped and well-financed commercial laboratories were able to turn the trick. Among his thousands of newspaper clippings there are several descriptions of modern work on synthetic diamonds, and I am convinced that, having read them, Emil imagined early work in his own laboratory along these lines.

2. Travel, in the opening years of this century and the end of the previous one, was a time-consuming affair, and the alleged journeys in 1897 and 1898 coincide with Chicago activities which Emil has described in considerable detail. Perhaps he was exploring the world during most of those two years rather than attending medical school, teaching chemistry, and treating enormous numbers of patients in Chicago, but he could not have been doing both.

3. If Emil kept a diary he did not preserve and transmit it to his biographer, although he did save such things as a pamphlet entitled "Complexol for the Complexion" which he had written

for the Helsey Brothers Company of Chicago and St. Paul and fourteen pamphlets written for the Chicago Pharmaceutical Company offering tablets, liquids, ointments, and suppositories calculated to cure constipation, colic, gonorrhea, pyelitis and cystitis, blood and nerve diseases, high blood pressure and arterial sclerosis, hemorrhoids, liver disease, hay fever, goiter, and eczema.

4. The best and perhaps only available type of U.S. Government identification letter to someone in authority in a foreign country would have been a passport, but—according to a double check by the U.S. Passport Bureau—he had none, nor did he preserve other types of documents.

5. Nowhere does Emil mention dates of departure or arrival or the names of vessels, and in the period after his marriage in 1899, there is no mention as to whether or not his wife Clara, accompanied him.

6. By his own testimony in other connections as well as by photographs of established date, the dermatitis on his hands healed promptly, and it was not until several years later that secondary changes appeared in his hands and elsewhere. These facts are directly opposed to the "Autobiography" statement that the alleged travels in 1897 and 1898 were occasioned by radiation-induced lesions.

Do the accounts of his travels assay a high percentage of pure metal, as was claimed by Emil in the case of the platinum-bearing sands of the Snake River, or do they run less than one eight-millionth of an ounce of metal per ton, which government records indicate to have been the true value in that instance?

Eight

1917 – 48: WORLD WAR I TO RETIREMENT

At the time the United States entered World War I, twenty-one years had elapsed since Roentgen's discovery of X-rays, but technical advances had been modest. Induction coils equipped with various types of interrupters had been the commonest sources of high-voltage current until quite late. W. D. Collidge's hot-cathode tube had barely begun to replace the conventional "gas tubes" which, although certainly better than the original Crookes tubes, nevertheless were erratic and inefficient. Films had not yet replaced glass X-ray plates, intensifying screens were poor and little used, and because Potter's ingenious application of Bucky's ideas about scattered radiation was still five years away, heavy parts such as the trunk and pelvis had to be examined piecemeal rather than by large plates if sharp images were desired. The enormous importance of X-rays in diagnosing diseases of the respiratory, alimentary, and urinary tracts was a phase of radiology which lay in the dim future, and only in the case of fractures and gunshot wounds did physicians and their patients regularly expect X-rays to be helpful. The usefulness of X-rays in treating skin cancer was established, but attempts to extend therapy to deep-seated cancer had backfired, and the procedure generally was in ill repute.

Even in the much older disciplines of surgery and internal medicine, protracted graduate training of the sort provided by present-day residency programs was available in only a few centers and attracted few candidates. Formal training in radiology, still far from recognition as a real section of medical science, was almost unknown, save for the peculiar variety offered by such institutions as Emil's Illinois School of Electro-Therapeutics.

These weaknesses were a serious handicap to American military leaders faced with the necessity of finding one or more "X-ray men" for each of the many teams that had to be put together to care for the anticipated flood of fractures and gunshot wounds. While vast numbers of recruits were being taught to be soldiers, a small peacetime professional army faced the dual problems of detailing considerable numbers to the training of recruits and yet sending as many as possible to Europe as stopgap assistance to our allies and token of the many more presently to come.

In medicine even this advance guard had to be drawn largely from civilian life. In the case of radiology, the supply of able-bodied radiologists of military age was so small that soon almost every one of them was serving in Europe, leaving so few for training others at home that presently some had to be called back and re-assigned to that work. Emil's failure to participate in this work is easily explained. The army's need was for X-ray diagnosis exclusively, and this was a field which by this time interested Emil almost not at all. If he was a radiologist to any extent, he was a radiation therapist; and of course his activities in electrology had no place at all in the military program.

At first schools of military radiology were conducted in several places, including Chicago and New York, but within a few months, all had been consolidated at Camp Greenleaf in Fort Oglethorp, Georgia, near Chattanooga, Tennessee. A few of the student officers trained at Greenleaf saw active duty in France, and practically all of them served for several months to more than a year at various military hospitals in which the wounded were rehabilitated and surveyed, preliminary to returning them to civilian life. All of them learned the advantages of co-operation between radiologists, surgeons, internists, and pathologists, and these colleagues in turn, learned to depend on the assistance of radiologists in their day-by-day work.

When physicians so conditioned resumed or established civilian practice, their ideas and needs exerted powerful influence on manufacturers, medical schools, medical societies, hospital boards, and patients, and the prewar type of radiology, so well known to Emil, passed out of existence in all but a few sheltered corners of medicine. Furthermore, the resumption of scientific contact with Germany brought word of 200-kilovolt generators and tubes, copper filters "to harden the beam," and the beginning of measuring devices which soon resulted in the establishment of the unit of dosage now known as the r (after Roentgen). These developments brought a new lease of life to radiation therapy but at the same time laid on its practitioners the necessity of acquiring a degree of proficiency in physics and mathematics beyond that available a quarter of a century earlier at Valparaiso.

Soon, too, Potter's grid, double-coated films, intensifying screens, better contrast media (first barium sulfate, replacing bismuth subcarbonate; then sodium iodide; and presently an endless procession of drugs of varying chemical composition but improved safety and effectiveness), and steadily improving tubes, generators, timing devices, etc., broadened the scope of X-ray diagnosis and improved its quality. Most important of all, residency training became available in numerous educational centers, and a board was established to certify the competence of those who practiced clinical radiology.

Throughout the United States, many radiologists of Emil's vintage or slightly younger adapted themselves to these changes and in many instances were active in bringing them about. The fact that Emil failed to adapt probably is explained in part by the fact that he was a homeopath. Hahnemann had closed by this time, and, although a homeopathic medical society continued for many years, the homeopathic group in Chicago must have felt the frustration common to individuals and groups facing extinction because of lack of progeny.

By the time of U.S. entry into World War II, graduate instruction in radiology had become so soundly established that it was not necessary for the armed services to train radiologists; instead, their educational activities were restricted to technicians. It was recognized also that, except for rather minor modifications that made for transportability, apparatus designed for civilian use was directly applicable to military needs. Surgery, meanwhile, had progressed to the point where the localization of metallic foreign bodies, which had been a major aim of World War I radiology, had become comparatively unimportant. As far as diagnosis was concerned, therefore, there was no repetition of the World War I situation where technical developments made necessary by the war modified subsequent civilian practice.

Radiation therapy, on the other hand, which blossomed in 1918 as a result of developments that had been going on inside Germany in spite of the shortages and harassments of World War I, flowered again and even more abundantly, when the wartime work of Robert Stone's large group at the University of Chicago and of scientists at Los Alamos and other atomic bomb centers was declassified at the close of World War II and the workers scattered to resume clinical activities. Many of Stone's group were radiologists, but many others belonged to a new category of colleagues working in fields closely allied to, but not identical with, radiology. These, of course, are the men and women—physicians, physicists, chemists, and biologists—who use radioisotopes clinically and experimentally. If Emil had been bewildered by the new clinical and physical concepts growing out of World War I radiology, that bewilderment was nothing compared with what he faced at the end of World War II. He liked to believe that he served as a consultant in such work, but there is record merely of the fact that he did serve as a civilian consultant in X-ray diagnosis to Chicago draft boards.

The possibility that Emil collaborated in radiological teaching at Johns Hopkins during World War I rests merely on his own statements, made many decades after the alleged fact, and cannot be substantiated by that institution's contemporary records or by contemporary letters, notes, or other written matter among his voluminous papers.

For more than three decades following World War I, Emil continued to practice a type of radiology that had been prevalent in an earlier age: such was not the case, however, elsewhere in the city of his birth. Several important advances had their genesis there and advances of all sorts were adopted promptly in leading Chicago hospitals and private offices.

At that time America's foremost large and small manufacturers of X-ray apparatus and accessories were located in Chicago, so that radiologists living there found it easy to approach manufacturers with ideas for improving the tools of their profession. Radiologists from other cities who traveled to Chicago to consult those manufacturers incidentally brought their ideas to the attention of Chicago radiologists somewhat earlier than might otherwise have been the case. With the years, the X-ray industry, like most of the nation's other manufacturing activity, underwent the merging, consolidation, and dispersal which seem to be essential to adequate financing, but from the standpoint of the users of X-ray equipment the change was not without its disadvantages.

One of the most important early centers of radiation therapy was Mercy Hospital, under the leadership of the late Dr. Henry Schmitz. Shortly after the end of World War I, Schmitz had studied in Freiburg with Krönig and Friederich, whose important monograph "The Physical and Biological Basis of Radiation Therapy," had been published in Germany in 1918. Returning from his studies, Schmitz prepared an English translation of the monograph, built a therapy center at Mercy, and for several years taught radiation therapy and practiced it.

At the University of Illinois, Dr. Hartung had used 400-kilovolt radiation as early as 1939, but that institution's most important contribution to therapy began with the arrival of Dr. Roger A. Harvey and the establishment of the first American betatron devoted to clinical work.

At about the time that Schmitz was promoting the German variety of radiation therapy at Mercy, Dr. Max Cutler began seven years of service at Michael Reese Hospital, emphasizing French methods and particularly the use of radium. A spectacular feature of this work was the installation of a teleradium unit, or so-called radium bomb, containing four grams of radium on loan from its Belgian owners. In 1938, Dr. Erich L. Uhlmann succeeded to the headship of the service, constructed a new institute building, and, in keeping with the times, shifted emphasis from radium to telecobalt applicators and a linear accelerator.

From 1938 until its removal to the University of Chicago in 1954, Dr. Cutler operated the Chicago Tumor Institute at 21 West Elm Street on the Near North Side, where he gathered a distinguished staff, including visiting radiation therapists and surgeons from France and England. Cutler accepted for therapy patients with almost any sort of neoplasm, but he and his institute were best known for the irradiation of laryngeal cancer.

Since 1954, the Chicago Tumor Institute had been incorporated as part of the Department of Radiology at the University of Chicago where its present Director, Dr. J. W. J. Carpender, and his staff work in close cooperation with Dr. Robert D. Moseley, Jr., Chairman of the Department, and Dr. Leon Jacobsen and other members of the staff of the University's Argonne Cancer Research Hospital.

With the years, the spotlight in the theater of cancer therapy has shifted from surgery to external radiation to isotopes, and rests at the moment on hormones and other chemical substances, with the work of Dr. Charles Huggins of the University of Chicago's Ben May Laboratory well in the forefront. But the stage is large, the actors numerous, and the subject broad; regardless of the location of the spotlight at any particular time, all of the actors play important roles and the work of all is needed if the clinical gains of the past are to continue in the future.

In the early years, Emil practiced X-ray diagnosis as well as therapy. In his scrapbooks are preserved illustrated newspaper accounts of his ministrations to prizefighters with broken hand bones and children who had swallowed toy camels. These scrapbooks contain, also, schedules of fees for X-ray examinations and advertisements of courses in his school in the Champlain Building. Elsewhere in Chicago, X-ray diagnosis was employed far earlier than Emil's statements indicate, and development continued long after he had lost interest in all but the therapeutic phases of radiology.

Chicago's enormous charity hospital, Cook County Hospital, must have begun X-ray diagnosis in 1896 or very shortly thereafter, because in the earliest records available to me, those for the year 1903, much is made of the fact that an "entirely new outfit for the X-ray laboratory had been obtained." This consisted of an induction coil of increased power, a rheostat, and several new X-ray tubes. The "Charity Service Reports" for the years 1904–7 are silent on the subject of X-rays, but in 1908 it is stated that "the X-ray laboratory has been placed in charge of a skilled professor in that branch of modern science." The equipment was said to be of the very latest design, consisting of six Crookes tubes of various sizes, a 15-inch Scheidel coil, mercury and electrolytic interrupters, and a fluoroscope.

At some time previous to 1917, Dr. E. L. Blaine had become head of the service. In that year, it is recorded, he examined 10,-000 patients with a staff consisting only of himself, one technician, two nurses, one darkroom technician, and a typist.

Dr. Francis C. Turley succeeded to the headship when Dr.

Blaine entered the army, to be followed by Dr. Baker, then by a non-physician, Mr. Arthur E. Willis, and in 1911 by the late Dr. Hartung who rendered distinguished service for many years. Hartung was followed in turn by Drs. Blaine, Mathewes, Warfield, Hubeny, and Landau, and at the time of this writing the work is in the charge of the able and popular Irvin F. Hummon, Jr., M.D.

Little information is available about radiology at Michael Reese Hospital between the years 1911 and 1915, but in September, 1915, the late Dr. Robert A. Arens began a service which continued for thirty-nine years. He had worked in St. Louis as an X-ray repair man and had received two years of medical education before coming to Chicago to join the staff at Reese. Six months after his coming, the head of the department resigned and Dr. Arens took over, working at the hospital and simultaneously attending the Chicago Medical College from which presently he obtained an M.D. degree. It is reasonable to assume that in the days before 1911 the institution owned small induction coils and gas tube outfits of the sort which were commonplace throughout the city and the country.

X-ray diagnosis at the University of Illinois is particularly noteworthy because of Dr. Hartung's early use of laminography and later because of the work of Drs. Percival Bailey, Paul Bucy, and others in the field of neuroradiology.

Previous to 1910, such radiology as was done at St. Luke's Hospital was in the hands of a non-medical technician; but in 1910 Dr. Van Horn was placed in charge, and three years later an arrangement was set up under which the distinguished gastrointestinal radiologist, Dr. James T. Case, commuted to St. Luke's weekly on Fridays from the Battle Creek Sanitarium in Battle Creek, Michigan. Shortly after 1913, Dr. C. L. Moir replaced Van Horn, to be followed in 1916 by Dr. Edward L. Jenkinson, who (except for leave of absence during World War I), served as head of the department until St. Luke's fused with Presbyterian in 1959.

In 1898 William and Edward Blair purchased and presented to Presbyterian Hospital its first X-ray equipment (cost, $438.33), and from then until 1906 Dr. Joseph S. Smith (affectionately known as "X-ray Smith") was in charge of the work. In 1903 the first apparatus was replaced by a more modern variety and Dr.

Smith was granted a salary of $40.00 a month plus half the net income from the department, up to a ceiling of $800 a year. Eventually he took surgical training in Vienna, and on returning settled in Wausau, Wisconsin, where he became recognized as an unusually able surgeon.

For the nine years from 1906 to 1915 the department was directed by Dr. Hollis Potter, then by Dr. Cassie Rose, and for the past many years, Dr. F. H. Squire, long recognized for general excellence in the practice and teaching of diagnostic radiology. Presbyterian is known particularly as one of the earliest institutions in the Midwest to pay serious attention to cardiovascular radiology.

After leaving Presbyterian Hospital, Dr. Hollis Potter practiced diagnostic radiology for many years in an office on Michigan Boulevard. His fame as a diagnostician spread beyond the city, but the development which has carried his name throughout the world and which undoubtedly constitutes Chicago's greatest contribution to radiology is his invention and personal construction of a moving grid for the suppression of scattered radiation which previously had made it impossible to obtain satisfactory large films of such parts as the trunk and the pelvis. Others had postulated that it was scattering which caused the troublesome blurring of the image in such films and had attempted to produce scatter suppressors, but without any practical success. Potter's contribution was the substitution of a curved grid made up of linear components from the earlier unsatisfactory cellular grids and the demonstration that when such a grid was interposed between patient and film and moved continuously during an X-ray exposure it not only absorbed scatter but left no image of itself to mar the image of the body part which was being examined. Only those who worked in radiology before 1920 can appreciate adequately what a stimulus Potter's work gave to the specialty.

The hospitals and medical school of the University of Chicago were latecomers in the field of radiology, coming into existence only in 1927. Growing as the entire medical program grew, the University's Department of Radiology, currently under the chairmanship of Dr. Robert D. Moseley, Jr., is most noteworthy for its undergraduate and graduate teaching, its research, and particularly the size of its senior staff, which makes possible a mature approach to various phases of radiology that would be quite impossible if a few staff members were required to spread themselves thinly over several fields. The diagnosis of bone diseases, techniques of gastrointestinal radiography, automatic timing of X-ray exposures, devices for protection against radiation hazards, and improvement of television-type X-ray image amplifiers are among the investigations and publications in the field of X-ray diagnosis of current and previous members of the department.

It is commonplace but nevertheless ill-advised to bemoan the fact that with specialization in radiology, as in other sections, we produce physicians who know more and more about less and less, and to long for the "good old days" when one competent doctor carried all necessary information under his hat. Such concepts amount to a contention that the welfare of the sick is best served by a static radiology. It is doubtful that anyone would defend such a contention when he, himself, was the patient.

Undoubtedly Emil had some sort of comprehension of what was happening in radiology following World War I, but his background did not serve him well in the surging intellectual turmoil of the mid-twentieth century. If he had graduated from such a place as the University of Michigan, had attended Rush, and had come under the influence of the great teachers of medicine clustered about the West Side hospitals at the turn of the century, probably he would not have "burned out" mentally and professionally as early as he did. But regardless of his native ability and the quality of his education, no physician can live as long as Emil did without eventually outliving his professional usefulness. The young men should take over, and they do; and the oldster who would stroll with them soon finds himself out of breath.

Nine

1948 – 60: RETIREMENT AND DEATH

In 1947 Emil Grubbe vacated the office he had been occupying at 6 North Michigan Avenue, and in 1948 he formally announced his retirement from practice. For a long time previously that practice had not been so active as to interfere with his avocation of writing to newspapers and magazines and fomenting interviews by professional writers; but with his world restricted almost exclusively to his two and one-half room seventh-floor apartment at 1205 West Sherwin Avenue, overlooking Lake Michigan, there was even more time for such activities, and he made the most of it. Increasingly frequent trips to hospitals for surgery were announced in advance to the press by means of "handouts" which always included a summary of his priority claims. He almost always declared himself to be the first man ever to have administered radiation therapy, the first ever to have suffered radiation injury, and the inventor of the fluoroscope, etc. For the most part these claims were printed in abbreviated form, but occasionally they were given *in extensio*, and not infrequently they led to the dispatch of reporters for interviews and photographs. Veteran reporters must have sensed the paucity of Emil's knowledge about contemporary medicine, including radiation, but presumably they pitied his deplorable infirmities and knew that their readers would relish a warm human-interest story. Unfortunately, however, some among the visiting newsmen were sufficiently unsophisticated to ask and record Emil's answers to such questions as the danger of fall-out, radiation in outer space, contamination in the neighborhood of nuclear reactors, and possible dangers inherent in television sets and luminous watch dials. That these were questions about which he was almost totally uninformed or even misinformed was appreciated by neither Emil nor his questioners, and national magazines, whose science editors should have known better, printed some of the interviews without expurgation. This led readers to write to the editors and to government agencies which in turn called forth replies. When harassed government agencies referred such correspondence to him, Emil misinterpreted this as evidence that the government, faced with problems that stumped its own experts, was obliged to him for help, and many readers apparently were of the same opinion. Informed physicians, physicists, and radiation biologists must have known that Emil was talking through his hat, but no one stepped forward to say so.

That is to be explained, no doubt, by our national custom of condoning harsh criticism of almost any living person who disagrees with us but deploring any criticism at all of the dead and extending that exemption to the very old, particularly if they are infirm.

In the past few decades the dangers inherent in the ingestion or inhalation of radium salts by those who paint them on luminous watch and clock dials has received much attention in the scientific and popular press. As the story unfolded, it appeared that a former practice of "pointing" with the lips the small brush used for such work was one of the most important contributing factors; there is no evidence that wearing luminous-dial wrist watches exposes the wearer to radiation hazard. Even in the extreme situation of an airplane cockpit, equipped with many dozens of radiumized dials, the doses delivered through instrument crystals becomes barely significant, but to meet this and similar possible trouble, strontium-90 generally has replaced radium. Emil, however, condemned all luminous dials and insisted that he had treated a patient who suffered radiation erythema from wearing such a watch.

He was impressed by the fact that carnotite, an ore from which radium is obtained as a byproduct of the recovery of metals used in hardening steel, is fairly prevalent in some of our western mountain states. He was convinced that animals and crops raised on such land stored radium, so that those who consumed them developed leukemia, and he urged the government to fence and padlock vast areas in the West as a means of stamping out leukemia. Television tubes constituted a serious radiation hazard, he believed, and he predicted a latent crop of erythematous noses among present-day children who press those members against the tube fronts of home television sets. Finally, he saw in the transistors of hearing aids still another radiation hazard.

In the matter of atomic fission (of course he called it "splitting the atom"), it amused and annoyed him to have the phenomenon spoken of as a development of World War II, because according to his contention he had done it all, including the clinical use of radioisotopes, as early as 1898.

Actually, studies of the distribution of leukemia show no increased incidence in the mountain states or elsewhere in the nation. There is not even a higher incidence of leukemia in southern India, where radioactivity of the soil is spectacularly high.

As to television sets, it is well recognized that during the manufacture of image tubes workers must be protected against a small amount of radiation, but unless and until tube voltages become much higher than they are at present, the risk to viewers is nonexistent. Transistors, of course, do not and cannot produce radiation.

As to "smashing the atom" and producing radioisotopes, Emil's totally false claims stem from two misconceptions to which he clung doggedly. First, he believed that the separation of free electrons from the solid aluminum cathodes of primitive X-ray tubes under bombardment by positive particles and the "boiling off" of electrons from the hot cathodes of Coolidge tubes constituted atomic fission, and, furthermore, that X-rays of even modest voltage on bombarding certain substances (for example, the headrest on a dental chair) rendered such substances radioactive. These beliefs are without foundation. Second, confusing fluorescence or phosphorescence with radioactivity, he believed quite falsely that when, in the early days of the century, he injected strontium salts into the tissues of his patients or dusted them on the skin surface, and followed this by exposure to X-rays, he was producing radioactive strontium. He considered it most unfair that present-day workers with genuine radio-strontium should be given credit which really belonged to him.

Even after he had gone for the last time from his home to the hospital he continued to communicate with the press and to receive deputations of various sorts. And, as usual, he made things difficult for the friends, physicians, nurses, and attendants who were striving to make him more comfortable. As the end drew near, there was a final flurry of activity during which he left the hospital against advice to go to what had been represented to him as a low-cost but high-quality nursing home. Before long, however, the new custodians agreed that the change had been unwise and brought him back to the hospital where, on March 26, 1960, he died, 85 years after his birth and 65 years after his first exposure to X-rays.

Dr. Grubbe's funeral oration, written in longhand some years before his death, did not come to light until several years later. Meanwhile, the actual funeral address had been given by the Reverend Alfred J. Johnson, Chaplain at the Swedish Covenant Hospital, in a chapel at 5303 North Western Avenue. Aware of his subject's atheism, Reverend Johnson contended that regardless of what Emil thought about religion, his life work had been in the service of mankind and was therefore of a truly Christian nature. He was candid, however, and when questioned by a reporter as to whether the deceased had recanted before death, he said he believed there had been no such deathbed change of view.

Readers who have persevered thus far with this little volume will appreciate how difficult it has been to present the man as he was in life without appearing unnecessarily to emphasize his shortcomings. His self-written funeral oration and the 83 self-written lines in the seventh edition of *Who's Who* are a sharper indictment than any I would be willing to draw up, but they are Emil's own words and he made it clear that he wished to speak them "from the grave." I reproduce them here, therefore, because they do reveal the man as almost nothing else could do, and also because to reproduce them is in accordance with his wishes.

Attached to the manuscript of the funeral oration were penciled notes reading:

> Put copy of biography of *Who's Who* with the paper you write which is to be read at your funeral. Biography is to be read after your paper has been read.
>
> In your funeral notice for the newspapers state that a formal message prepared by Dr. Grubbe, giving his philosophy of life, will be read by Dr. Alfred Lewy.
>
> Funeral notice in the newspapers: Grubbe, Dr. Emil H. Dr. Grubbe wrote his own funeral message which will be read by Dr. Alfred Lewy. Burial at Rosehill Mausoleum.

89

Emil H. Grubbe

(To add to obituary to be sent in advance with photo to all newspapers): Dr. Emil H. Grubbe (internationally known as the originator of the treatment of disease with x-rays).

Dr. Grubbe's Self-Written Funeral Oration

Many years ago I decided that when I die I would not have the funeral service usually allotted one who shuffles off this mortal coil. Naturally, since I was not a religionist, I did not want the services of a preacher nor the singing or playing of church hymns; in short, I did not want anything religious about this service.

And so I wrote my own funeral message which will be delivered to you through the kindness of my long-time friend, Dr. Alfred Lewy.[1]

But first, if any of you care to say anything about me on this occasion you may do so now; I won't hear you and, therefore, you can say what you please. Dr. Lewy will act as moderator.

And now, as Dr. Lewy reads what I have written, try to imagine that I am facing you and speaking.

Most men when they die are satisfied to be rated by what they own; I would rather be rated by what I think. So, as a final favor, I want you to listen to me even though I dare to differ with you.

Some who are here will not be surprised at what I say, but others, I am sure, will not only be surprised but possibly shocked.

I hope as friends of mine none of you will be offended at the language I use. I don't mean to be personally offensive; I merely state my beliefs, and you must admit that I have the right to do that even though what I believe disagrees with what you believe.

I grant that you have the right to your opinions, but you can't deny me the right to question them, and for the same reason I am entitled to express my opinions, even though they differ from yours.

Although most of you know that I was irreligious, few of you ever heard me use the plain, blunt words which I will use today. Even though I may shock some of you, I hope you will excuse me, for I have thought about the subject many years. I have not been biased for I have studied all

---

[1] Dr. Lewy died in December, 1958, more than a year before Emil did.

phases of the subject and, therefore, have a right to my conclusions and opinions.

Because of the intolerance of many on the subject, I have until now restrained myself from openly expressing my opposition to the forces of bigotry and bunk which sail under the name of religion. However, now I wish to speak my mind. The fact that others accept so-called spiritual ideas without thinking is no reason why I also should have done so.

Yes, I reserved for myself the right to evaluate life, to study the material universe, and to interpret reality as the accumulated facts of science and my own reason determined.

I stood for the liberation of the human mind from the bondage of ignorance fostered by so-called authority which bases its dogmas on beliefs, on tradition, and superstitions rather than facts. I preferred to deal with the facts. I wanted to be as independent of human vagaries and confusion as reason and common sense could make possible. I stood for an open-minded search for truth, the use of logic and free reason, regardless of the consequences which such rationality might have on the prejudices and mythical explanations of so-called authority. In other words, I preferred to substitute facts and straight thinking for faith and, therefore, I was irreligious.

I believe that every person should be free to have whatever religion he wishes or, if he prefers, he need have no religion at all. I chose to have no religion.

If I scoff at your beliefs, please forgive me. Since there are more than 2,750 different religions in the world, how can it be sacrilegious to discuss religion in general or any creed in particular? To show how important I considered this matter, I must tell you that I made a serious study of all major religions before I arrived at my conclusions.

By the way, how did you acquire your religion? Did you study all religions and then after that pick the one which you now acknowledge or did you inherit what you believe?

I was a scientist. A scientist is not controlled by his emotions when arriving at conclusions. Facts and straight thinking based upon all the available data are the only elements which concern him when he formulates his final conclusions. And so, I chose to put my faith in reality rather than in the illusions of a so-called spirituality. Even without the aid of science, my common sense revolted against the assumptions of the dogmas of the churches.

I believed that although the subject of religion has no material basis, its values should be determined and evaluated by the process of logic and reason just the same. In all other subjects, reason is the ultimate factor in determining and measuring value, so why not apply reason to religious matters also. Only in that way will man arrive at sane and valid answers. Other methods may give solace or emotional uplift and comfort, but if truth is thereby sacrificed, of what profit is it to the religionist?

The religionist who believes in one or more personal gods looks upon the universe of which he is an insignificant part through his feelings or emotions instead of facts interpreted by his sense and reason. On the other hand, the atheist studies the facts unearthed by science and history; he lives in a world of reality and consequently, the arguments of the religionist appear shallow and irrational to him.

The usual declaration of faith of the average religionist, such as belief in one or more personal gods, Jesus, Holy Ghost, the fall of man, redemption, the influence of prayer, the origin of the Ten Commandments, Heaven, Hell, angels, the Devil, the soul, a hereafter, resurrection, immortality, the holiness of the Bible, I could take no stock in.

Since all of these beliefs are unreasonable, they were, therefore, absurd to me.

I could not believe in the personal God of the Christian —a God who possesses all the human passions, such as love and hate; a God who is cruel and vindictive; a God who is presumed to know everything and, therefore, to be all wise, yet expects me—one of two billion human beings in this world—to beg him each day of my life to not only take care of me but to treat me better than my neighbors. I could not imagine a God who possesses common human frailties, such as elation and anger. I could not imagine a God who rewards the good and punishes the bad when both creatures are presumed to be of his own fashioning and their every act controlled by him. I could not imagine a God exhibiting love to some human beings and pitiless vengeance to others. I could not imagine a God who would create a Devil to pester me all of my living days and build a fiery Hell to burn my material body after I died. I could not imagine a God who made bad human beings when He could have made them all good.

To me, the whole idea of the personal God of the Christian is irrational, and what does not make sense makes nonsense.

I took no stock in the idea that a personal God conceived the notion that one human being, though innocent, had to suffer and die on the cross for all the sins of all the billions and billions of sinners who ever lived or will ever live upon this earth; an idea that is not only ethically wrong but revolting to common sense as well as reason. To a person who thinks straight, the idea of a man named Jesus, whose death by crucifixion nearly 2,000 years ago was (according to church dogma) to save sinners is one of the most irrational ideas ever proposed in the name of religion, and I never swallowed that.

Also, as a physician, I know how the human race is propagated and I never could see how any sane adult person, especially a physician who makes a serious study of anatomy, physiology, and biology, could believe in the idea of the Immaculate Conception of the child named Jesus.

It was always my opinion that any physician who believed in the dogma of the Immaculate Conception ought to have his license to practice medicine revoked.[2]

I could not believe that the wisdom of the human race, acquired in its most primitive and, therefore, most ignorant period—that is, the biblical period—should have better standing than the wisdom of the ages during which science taught man the facts of reality. I could not believe that all the wisdom to be found in the universe was in the possession of those who wrote the Bible. I also could not believe that all the wisdom that mankind has acquired since the Bible was written was anticipated by the writers of the book and that, therefore, the wisdom which man has obtained during the past 2,000 years is worthless. In other words, I could take no stock in a religion which assumes that all the material facts of the universe, as well as all the facts of human life, are completely considered and accurately chronicled in a book known as the Bible. I could not accept an inspired Bible. I rejected Christian as well as other forms of supernaturalism. To me, the Bible was a wholly man-made book which expressed the myths and superstitious notions of a bygone and very ignorant age. Neither could I accept the Bible as a moral guide. As a rationalist, I believed nothing which denies the evidence of facts and their verification or which excludes the use of common sense as well as logical thinking. Naturally, I rejected the biblical creation idea which concerns itself with a God who could make Adam a man and then, after starting to make a woman, ran out of material and so had to remove one of Adam's ribs in

---

[2] E.H.G. makes here one of the commonest of all errors of the uninformed writing about religious matters. The dogma of the Immaculate Conception, of course, has nothing at all to do with the birth of Christ, but rather with the birth of Mary.

order to finish the job of making woman. Such stuff has no sense behind it and is, therefore, an insult to my intelligence. I felt that all the arguments of the religionists were childishly shallow and did not deserve any respect on my part. To me, what did not make sense made nonsense. I was never childish enough to believe that prayers to an imaginary personal God would alter events. Neither could I believe that a provident God watched over me if I were good and destroyed me when I was not good. I could not accept such childish and irrational notions as the power of prayer, the fall of man, original sin . . . redemption by faith and the performance of miracles. Although the church has believed in and preached these dogmas for nearly 2,000 years, no facts to prove without question any of these doctrines have ever been produced. Unless such proof is available, no serious scientist can become a devout religionist. The whole idea of such a God ruling the universe is irrational and what doesn't make sense is nonsense. I, therefore, considered the Christian's conception of God nonsense and, to me, it was nothing but bunk. I could take no stock in the cruel, vindictive God of the Christians. A personal God as the creator of the universe as postulated by the religious cults I took no stock in. For me, that is a childish idea. The childishness of this idea will appear when I ask the question, "Who made your God?"

I believe the church and the preachers do harm to mankind when they state that man's sole purpose on this earth is to glorify a personal God. They keep the religious adherent so busy praising their imaginary God that there is no time for him to acquire a liberal education and become intelligent enough to understand himself and the universe about him. Reforms of social evils as well as advancement in all of life's activities will only come from education. The church has had nearly 2,000 years of man's time, most of it devoted to the glorification of God, but the accomplishment has been nil. The devout religionist is certain that when he dies and is buried here on earth that he will live again in another place. The rationalist claims that no human being has any knowledge of an after-life. He says that so far as anybody who is rational knows, when man dies he is dead and remains so. When his body disintegrates chemically, as is the case with all other cellular things, that's the finish of the individual.

My philosophy of life has been based on experience, not only my own experience but that of other individuals. I did not elude myself or waste much time with empty, imaginary or unreal vagaries of thought. The knowable always interested me more than did the unknowable. The study of reality always appealed to me more than did the fictitious study of spirituality. Life here on earth rather than a fictitious second life somewhere else seemed to me most important. If we study the facts of reality and the natural sciences, if we are unafraid to think straight, that is to think rationally, we must come to the conclusion that life on this planet is an unintelligent affair which is not operated with particular regard for man. If you question this statement, I will ask you to give reasons or an explanation for the cruelties chargeable in their entirety to nature. Man's helplessness before the forces of nature you all have knowledge of. When nature uses her forces, she is not concerned with man's wishes. She does as she pleases, as her whims determine. Ultimately, because she has no feelings nor emotional leanings toward man, nature destroys not only all that man has made or accomplished but also man himself. In other words, nature does not care whether man lives a happy, comfortable life or a cruelly painful life; she is absolutely indifferent. To me, all religion rests on supernaturalism. It can't be anything but imaginary nonsense. In other words, all religion is bunk, since science can find no proof that supernaturalism exists.

Wishful thinking and the use of the wild imagination will not give us any sane information about the purpose of life. Conclusions based upon everything but straight thinking—reasons, realism—may give us a pleasing answer to this question but it will not be the truth. Careful observation, worldly experience and logical reasoning alone will supply the proper answer. To all of us life is a bundle of uncertainties; to most of us life is a constant struggle; to many of us, it is a tragedy. My life efforts have been devoted to helping mankind fight one of nature's greatest cruelties—that is, disease—and one of man's greatest time-wasters—that is, religious bunk. In spite of the years of pain, I have found life interesting. My only regret is that time was fleeting, that there were not enough hours in the day, and that life was too short.

Man's life is brief and, as far as controlling the forces of nature is concerned, usually unimportant. Ultimately, everything, including man, will come to an end. Nature in the form of matter is the only omnipotent entity in the universe. Without any precepts, morals, or preconceived plan or method, she carries on.

I am to be taken to Rosehill Mausoleum where I will be among many of my friends of earlier days. I am to be interred in the mausoleum at Rosehill Cemetery, not underground but several feet above ground where you, my friends, will place me and where I will remain for some time. Yes, I will remain right here in Chicago with you. I mean by that, that I am not going to the Christian's Heaven, neither am I going to his Hell, wherever these two places may be located.

One more parting word. Some day you too, every one of you, will share my destiny and now good luck to all of you here assembled. May you before you die have at least some of the success and happiness which you have longed for.

Emil would have approved the newspaper coverage devoted to his death, to the funeral service, and to the subsequent entombment in crypt B 29 in the Community Mausoleum at Rosehill Cemetery, and he would have been pleased with the obituary which Dr. Benjamin Orndoff wrote for the September, 1960, number of *Radiology* (see Appendix II).

I had been informed that the crypt was among things which Emil had accepted from patients in lieu of cash during the depression years, but the story proved to be apocryphal. He bought it in 1915, paying $350 in quarterly instalments, the final payment being receipted November 26, 1915, and the warranty deed dated four days later.

Postscript

Over the ages there have been a few men and women so truly great that their reputations are immune to the bias or ineptitude of individual biographers. If one biography dwells with too much emphasis on the clay-like nature of their feet and another bestows halos or wings where none belong, little harm is done because still other biographies will follow and eventually from the whole, the truth will emerge. It is the solitary biography which is dangerous to reputations, and since the obscure unlike the great can expect at most a single biography they should, if they are wise, elect oblivion rather than risk the ministrations of a solitary and particularly an amateur biographer.

Emil Grubbe certainly was obscure, and by my criteria he was unwise as well because he insisted that this biography be written. I have taken the job seriously and to the best of my ability have portrayed the man as he really was; one of us; one of the world's all too plentiful ordinary people; vain, boastful, incompletely truthful, and only moderately able. This is far from the image he built for himself, an image which an uncritical contemporary press handed back to him (frequently as a result of his own skilful prodding) rearranged, gilded, and sometimes garbled. In this image he was scientist, investigator, martyr; but actually he was none of these except as one uses "martyr" colloquially to mean a "great or constant sufferer, as from disease." He was not consciously a charlatan but, like some actors who have devoted a lifetime to dramatic roles, he carried posturing and phraseology from his own personal stage into everyday life. Even stellar billing in "The Grubbe Story" was not enough. He was, in addition, copywriter, press agent, and advertising manager.

If this were all that could be said I should have abandoned my biographical assignment, writing off the hours spent wading through voluminous, disorganized papers as my contribution to blessed oblivion for my subject; but there is more. Out of my reading has come the picture of a man enormously concerned

97

with immortality. Only in early boyhood was the yearning satisfied by the promises of his family's Lutheran faith, but by young manhood this had been replaced by vituperative atheism undiluted by contact with enlightened religious teachers of his day and fanned by articles in the Sunday supplements of the more lurid of the Chicago newspapers and in the antireligious journals to which he subscribed.

Eventually he convinced himself that the immortality he was seeking lay in enshrining his name among the medical great and, having reached that decision, he allowed nothing to stand in the way. Always a careful man with a dollar, he now became frankly miserly, hoarding income from practice and business ventures and spending as little as possible on himself. Friends were allowed and, in fact, encouraged to provide him gratis materials and services they could afford less well than he, governmental and other agencies were importuned to remit taxes and bestow pensions, and, when patients were unable to pay their bills in cash, he accepted other things of value.

After some years of inquiry and consideration, he set up an arrangement under which the University of Chicago names part of its radiation therapy program for him and the Chicago Medical Society conducts a lectureship and grants a medal in his name.

Shall we call him egomaniac? Shall we emphasize the accidental, non-scientific, ill-advised nature of his early use of X-rays for the treatment of disease? Shall we make much of the fact that in no true sense does modern radiation therapy stem from his pioneer work?

I think there is no advantage in doing any of these things; instead, we should remember him for attributes which have become rare in modern society. Let us remember him rather for self-sufficiency, self-confidence, tenacity, and for a lust for life so great that it enabled him to contrive if not immortality at least long survival for the name of Emil H. Grubbe.

Appendix 1

The Value of a Static Machine
to the General Practitioner

In this age of progressiveness, when the laity determine largely the kind of study to which a physician must apply himself, it becomes necessary, in order to be considered a progressive and up-to-date physician to be able to treat patients with the latest therapeutic developments. Narrow-mindedness on the part of the physician means self-destruction.

It is true that the difficulties which arise in the use of static electricity as a therapeutic agent are multiplied and complex, but if physicians will use care, have a little perseverance and give attention to details, their efforts will be crowned with success, even beyond their expectation.

The beginner in the study of electricity will first learn that electrotherapy is not a new thing. Second that static electricity as a therapeutic agent is one of the oldest; that is, has brought about results which were almost miraculous when other therapeutic means have failed; that progress in this line of late has been even greater than in the great field of surgery.

Until recently the therapeutic value of static electricity was not appreciated, because its physiological action was little understood.

Practically the study of this form of electricity is in its infancy, yet it is surprising how broad a therapeutic field it has already developed and how many cases can be relieved by its application.

It has been truthfully said that "No instrument or set of instruments has such a wide range of usefulness as a static machine."

If you have any doubts as to the possibilities of this form of electricity, locate some colleague who possesses a static machine and who knows how to use it; have him tell you a few things about this force, or better, have its powers demonstrated upon your own person.

The study of this agent from a physiological standpoint will surprise physicians who are not familiar with it. The future indicates that as a therapeutic measure it is destined to be one of the most important. No other has the suggestion of greater possibilities, and the medical profession of the future, to succeed, will be compelled to have knowledge of this great force.

Reprinted from the *Alkaloidal Clinic*, April, 1901.

Without going into the various methods of administering this form of electricity to the different diseases or conditions to which it may be applied, a general consideration may be advisable, but in so short a paper we can only mention, in a cursory manner, a few of the diseases and conditions in which static electricity is indicated and in which it will usually bring most excellent results.

Above all it is a regulator of the functions of the body. Its greatest activity is manifest upon those functions which have to do with metabolism—the modification of nutritive processes. Because of this action it is the greatest stimulant and tonic we know of. It equalizes the circulation in general.

Since most functional ailments are caused by disturbances of normal circulation or of normal innervation we can readily see how it is that static electricity does its work.

It has achieved especially brilliant results in the diseases which are usually classified as chronic. No other therapeutic agent can compare with it in the treatment of nervous affections. It is easily applied, and as the removal of the clothing is not necessary, it is exceedingly pleasant to the patient.

In all varieties of gout, rheumatism and arthritis the efficiency of this form of electricity has been tested and found to be unequalled.

In gynecology it has even outdone galvanism and faradism in the relief of many distressing ailments of women. Especially is this the case in dysmenorrheas, amenorrheas, pelvic, adhesions and chronic inflammatory conditions, and at the menopause no remedy elicits more frequent expressions of satisfaction or gives more speedy and permanent relief.

It is the remedy par excellence in epilepsy, chorea, hysteria and other mental disturbances. Nurasthenia or nervous exhaustion, a condition which, because of its great variety of symptoms, is a puzzle to the physicians, will be improved immediately under the influence of static electricity.

Even such profound diseases as diabetes, bright's disease and paralysis agitans may be decidedly relieved and in many cases entirely cured by its application. In locomotor ataxia sometimes one single treatment will do more to relieve the "lightning pains" and "crises" than any other remedy, not excepting morphine. Patients are made comfortable and actually say they find life worth living again.

Most surprising results have been obtained in paralysis and atrophies. Whole areas and groups of muscles have once more been restored to complete power.

Because of its well known power to improve the richness and purity of the blood, it is of undoubted value in anemia and chlorosis and all diseases due to impaired nutrition.

No other one remedy has earned as much praise in the relief of neuralgic pains, sciatica and lumbago. Its control over the muscular and nervous system is supreme.

Many skin diseases including those of the scalp yield to static treatment. It allays pain in any part of the body and as a remedy for insomnia it is unrivaled.

From the foregoing it will be seen that there are but few diseases or conditions in which static electricity cannot be used with great benefit. Although it is not the intention to leave the impression that static electricity is a "cure-all," yet we find many patients who have run the gauntlet; have tried everything without relief, these I believe we should give the benefit of a trial of this form of electricity.

We have not by any means enumerated all the different diseases and conditions to which static electricity is applicable, but it is not necessary to further laud its benefits. They speak for themselves. We venture to assert that no progressive physician can do full justice to himself and many of his patients without its help.

If physicians will conscientiously study this force, the brilliant results obtained in practice will remunerate them for their trouble and they will have become familiar with one of the most potent therapeutic agents ever given to the science of medicine.

In addition to the use of the static machine for general therapeutic work, another and equally important feature is its applicability for X-ray work.

Therefore the possession of a powerful static machine enables the physician to combine treatment with diagnosis. Today radiography is universally recognized as the best and only absolute method of diagnosing fractures and dislocations, also in localizing foreign bodies and abnormal growths in any part of the body. We may examine the lungs, the liver and brain. The stomach may be definitely outlined by means of the X-ray, and its size, shape and position determined. The position of such bodies as bullets, pins and needles, because of their great density, is of course easily detected. The extent of an aneurism of the aorta may be determined before physical signs appear. In fact the X-ray has opened up the greatest field of the century in the matter of diagnosis and therapeutics. Even the most skeptical concede the value of an X-ray outfit to diagnose fractures from dislocations, incorrect diagnosis of which by the ordinary methods usually results in lawsuits.

There is no doubt as to the value of the X-ray also used as a therapeutic agent. In the treatment of skin diseases it has already developed to a greater degree. The various conditions of acne, eczema, sycosis, herpes, hypertrichosis, favus and chronic œdema have been relieved and those most formidable diseases—cancer and lupus—which have resisted everything else have yielded, and almost marvelous results have been obtained by the aid of the X-ray.

Under its influence combined with other static currents the numerous cases of consumption of which every practitioner knows may be decidedly benefited.

An X-ray outfit will pay for itself in a short time. The practitioner is more liable to lawsuits now than heretofore, in fact, it seems that there are unscrupulous patients and lawyers who devote most of their time to damaging the reputations of physicians. In order to protect himself the physician should be able to apply every possible means to correct diagnosis. The importance of the fact that one is able by means of the X-ray to diagnose a fracture from a dislocation without any doubt, is self-evident. But aside from the medico-legal aspect it is a medium capable of being used for diagnosing many diseases in which physical signs are very doubtful. The discovery of renal and vesical calculi by radiography has been demonstrated in many cases and proved by operation.

Because of the great variety of uses to which a static machine may be applied we must conclude that there is no one other therapeutic apparatus which the physician uses, which will bring him more speedy success, financial remuneration to himself, and relief to his suffering patient, than a static machine. A young physician just starting out can make no better investment, if he can spare the money, than by supplying himself with a complete static and X-ray outfit. It gives him a superior standing at once, not only among the people of the community, but the physicians in his locality recognize in him a valuable addition to the profession.

X-Rays in the Treatment of Cancer and Other Malignant Diseases

Realizing that the reporting of immature results and deductions has been the bane of current medical literature, we have deferred giving for publication our experience with the x-rays in the treatment of malignant diseases because we wished to give the remedy the test of time. Since, however, so many articles have appeared lately upon this subject, based upon the reports of a few isolated and indefinitely stated cases with poor histories, we venture, at the risk of being accused of prematurity, to express our opinion upon the therapeutics of the x-ray.

This is only a preliminary report, but the writer wishes to state that

Reprinted from the *Medical Record* (New York: William Wood, 1902).

the conclusions herein arrived at are not based upon cases of doubtful diagnosis, for most of them have been post-operative, and, therefore, the question of diagnosis is not an open one. We have treated with the x-ray, during the larger part of the past year, an average of over seventy patients each day, which we believe to be the largest number of daily x-ray treatments yet reported by any individual. Having had such a large number of cases to study from, and doing pioneer work in this line, we have, of course, formed some opinion of the value of the treatment; and although we do not wish to be understood as announcing this as our final opinion, owing to the fact that time may materially change it, we present what we have learned to the profession for what it may be worth.

The use of the x-ray as a therapeutic agent is not so new as many would suppose; in fact, several x-ray operators have patients now under observation who were discharged symptomatically cured by the x-ray more than two years ago.

At first the treatment was taken largely on faith, but now, facts, illustrating the value of the x-ray as a therapeutic agent, appear in nearly every issue of most medical journals, and it must be familiar to every one that an agent which can at once demand the attention of so many minds from all parts of the world, must have some merit. Have the results obtained by dozens of different writers in treating hundreds of cases all been exceptional? Have they all been spontaneous cures? Certainly not. The only logical conclusion which it is possible to form is, that there must be great value in the use of the x-ray for therapeutic purposes.

As a remedy for lupus, this treatment has successfully passed through the crucial test of practical experience. None who have experience will gainsay that. Since it is a fact conceded by everybody who has investigated the subject, that trophic changes, such as dermatitis, exfoliation of the skin, falling off of the hair and nails, result from exposure to x-rays, and since it is also a fact that lupus and epithelioma are cured, clinically at least, by the x-rays, why may not this agent be of value in the more malignant or deeper-seated affections?

Aside from the speculative part of the value of the x-ray, it certainly is perfectly logical, from every standpoint, to suppose that if we admit that tuberculosis of the skin is curable, which we must from statistics at hand, tuberculosis of the lungs or the bones, and other forms of this disease must be amenable to x-ray treatment, for tuberculosis conditions are similar in whatever part of the body they may be found. Again, if we admit that epitheliomas are curable by the x-ray— and no one in the present light of things can doubt that—we can also suppose that cancer in any other part of the body is amenable to this treatment. First, because cancer tissue is primarily the same in whatever part of the body it may be found, being composed of epithelial cells; and, second, because of the ability of the x-ray to penetrate tissue there is no part of the body which is beyond its reach.

Many theories have been advanced as to the action of the x-ray in the various conditions for which it has been used. By some the belief is held that restitution of the tissues takes place under x-ray treatment; that is, cancer tissue becomes transformed or is developed into normal tissue. Others, taking for granted that the parasitic or bacterial theories of the origin of some of the diseases treated by the x-ray have been conclusively proven, believe that the x-ray, due to its actinic action, destroys these conditions. These theories seem rather farfetched, however, for, aside from the lack of proof of the parasitic or bacterial origin of the diseases referred to, it does not seem probable, from observations which have been made by various investigators, that the success of the x-ray treatment in these diseases is exclusively due to any bactericidal power which the rays may possess.

Personally, we believe the action of the x-ray is the same in all the diseases in which it has been found of value, and also that that action is most plausibly explained when viewed from the standpoint of the theory of phagocytosis followed by leucocytolysis.

First, it must be admitted that, aside from whatever chemical or electric property the x-ray may possess, the sum total of its action is that of an irritant. Now if we irritate a certain part of the body by making frequent x-ray exposures, we produce ultimately a simple focal inflammation. Inflammation means the determination of much blood to the part, hyperæmia. Due to the increased volume of blood, leucocytes accumulate in large quantities and, finally, stasis occurs, the circulation being cut off, the part dies for want of nourishment. When no suitable nutritive material is at hand there is developed a tendency toward degeneration. No doubt this degeneration is partly, at least, due to an accumulation of the products of the metabolism of cells.

Primarily, then, the x-ray affects the essential tissue-forming elements of the body. The parts which are walled off decompose chemically and are either discharged or absorbed. The rapid decrease in the size of some growths under x-ray treatment also points to a more general or systemic action, probably due to stimulation of the lymphatics.

The fact that nearly every case, no matter how severe, treated by the x-ray seems to improve at the beginning of the treatment, shows that it exerts an influence which is not only local but also systemic. From our personal observations upon several hundred patients we have come to the conclusion that the nutrition of the entire system is affected, through reflex action probably, and this produces a general stimulating and tonic effect. As to the special characteristics of the x-ray in different conditions our experience teaches that the vitality of all patients is increased. It is surprising how long life may be maintained in some cases. Relief from pain is found in the majority of cases, although if a neuritis is coexistent with cancer, especially in breast cases, very little can be done for the relief of the pain.

Tuberculous conditions, especially lupus vulgaris, have been most favorably affected by the x-ray. In our own use of this agent the following is the relative order in which we should classify the diseases for which the x-ray treatment has been given, and the order in which we should expect results, relatively: lupus, epithelioma, nodular returns (postoperative), primary breast cases, tuberculosis of the lungs, tuberculosis of the bones, cancers of soft internal organs, sarcomas, osteosarcomas.

In making this classification we do not wish to assert that all the above-named conditions have positively been cured by x-ray treatment. Statistics to that effect are not yet at hand. We are not optimistic enough to assert that all cancers can be permanently arrested or cured by this or any other known method of treatment, but we do believe that the x-ray has established for itself a field in the therapeutics of lupus and epithelioma. Not only that, but the future will see its greatest application in the treatment of patients immediately after operation, to prevent the possibility of recurrence.

Without in any way wishing to depreciate the splendid work of surgery, we must say that recurrences are only too numerous. It is a well-known fact that in only a small percentage of the cases of cancer operated upon does the growth fail to return. Concerning the status of the value of the surgical treatment of carcinoma, we quote from an editorial in the *Medical Record* of April 5, 1902, in which it is said that "we know our limitations in the radical surgery of carcinomatous diseases, and we recognize the fact that our best efforts do not cure, but only in a small proportion of cases annihilate the neoplasm."

It is not recommended that the x-ray take the place of the knife in primary or operable malignant growths, but the results so far obtained by x-ray treatment following operation are certainly sufficient to warrant the careful consideration of the profession. In general, the results of x-ray treatment speak for themselves, and it is unnecessary to present here any argument concerning the practicability of the use of this agent. Enough has already appeared upon this in medical literature.

It may be well, however, to point out that the whole matter resolves itself into the question of a proper understanding of x-ray phenomena. It is the correct use of this agent for special conditions, with ability to vary its power when necessary, that is essential for obtaining proper results, and not its use in the haphazard manner which is so common today, when, through ignorance of its virtues, the x-ray, which is hailed as a triumph by the physician in his struggle against tuberculous and cancerous conditions, becomes a dangerous force in the hands of the incompetent operator. We must not forget that we have a great variety of x-rays to deal with—in fact, to use a comparison, the variation in quantity and quality of x-rays obtainable with one piece of apparatus is much greater than all the varieties and qualities of tones which may be produced upon the keyboard of a piano. Again, different tissues demand different degrees of x-ray value.

When we understand these facts we can readily see why the treatment of an epithelioma must be different from the treatment of lupus. Ignorance of these facts probably accounts for much of the difference of opinion which exists to-day regarding the therapeutic value of the x-ray.

A few words concerning the so-called x-ray "burns." The continued administration of the x-ray in any one locality produces, at first, through its irritating influence, a dermatitis. If the treatments are unduly continued, ulceration of the tissues may occur, but an x-ray "burn" need never be considered serious. This statement is made because of the many bold announcements which have appeared concerning the "dangers of burning under x-ray exposure." Relatively, the inflammatory reaction, or dermatitis, produced by the x-ray is harmless, and, in most cases, if the parts were not meddled with by the application of strong chemicals, especially carbolic acid in some form or other (which, of itself, may cause gangrene), nature would assert her power and make repairs. We believe we have "burned" every patient treated, and several of them have been "burned" repeatedly. Concerning the development of the dermatitis, we find that susceptibility varies considerably. Certain individuals develop a decided reaction after the first treatment, whereas others resist the action of the rays to such a degree that it is only after from one to two months of daily treatment that we are able to develop a reaction. In one case daily treatments have been given for over two years, and, although the tube has been placed very near the body, nothing more than a slight redness has developed. It is evident from this that an idiosyncracy must exist.

To prevent the action of the rays upon surrounding tissues, a special lead-foil mask is used, which resists the passage of rays to healthy parts. Another precaution might be recommended, in order that the "burning" stage may be retarded—it is the application of plain vaselin to the parts exposed directly to the rays. This substance retards the superficial irritation very much, and is especially useful when treating the deeper tissues, and when there is no open ulcer. In all open or broken-down conditions a dermatitis should be rapidly produced.

The following are brief reports of a few cases:

CASE I.—Mrs. M., aged forty years, recurrent carcinoma of right breast. Radically operated upon first time in August, 1900. Recurrence immediately, followed by second operation. Six months after second operation nodules again began to appear in scar tissue, and third operation was performed. After this the nodules remained away for nearly one year, but finally they appeared again, and the patient undertook x-ray treatment. The whole scarred area was filled with a large number of small nodules, each about the size of a pea, which extended even into the axilla. Under x-ray treatment these nodules gradually began to fade away. The patient's appetite improved, pains disappeared, and she felt stronger, and was visibly improved in general health, so much so that her friends constantly inform her of her improvement. In this case the treatment was not taken as regularly as recommended. Sittings were given daily for about one month, and on alternate days for nearly four months. Although we do not consider this patient absolutely cured, she certainly shows so much improvement that we think we are justified in calling this a symptomatic or clinical cure.

CASE II.—Mrs. L., aged forty-eight years, case of scirrhous cancer of right breast. Three years ago last January a small hard tumor was noticed, which was painful to the touch. Her physician suspected a malignant condition on account of the family history, and an operation was performed, the breast being removed. Last August three nodules began to develop simultaneously in the operation scars. These nodules grew quite rapidly, and since another operation was refused, patient was recommended by her surgeon to try x-ray treatment, which was accordingly begun on September 5, last. Treatment was given daily until November 15, when decided dermatitis developed. The patient was allowed to rest until December 5, when treatments were begun once more, and continued daily until January 20, at which time all three of the nodules had entirely disappeared. This case also presented a condition of keloid, which extended over an area of six inches, and which also was very markedly affected by the x-ray exposures.

CASE III.—Mrs. O., aged fifty-six years, cancer left breast—so diagnosed by several prominent physicians who had treated her. The original growth presented an ulcerated surface measuring seven by five and one-half by two inches. Several severe hemorrhages had taken place, and patient was very weak. Discharge foul and very profuse. Glands in axilla swollen and very tender. Pain in growth and surrounding parts constant and, at times, excruciating. Many methods of treatment had been tried during a period of nearly three years, but were found to be of no value, the condition gradually getting worse. Finally, x-ray treatment was advised and undertaken. Treatment given every other day for twenty minutes. No improvement or effect was noticed, other than relief from pain, until after the third week of treatment, when decided dermatitis had developed and pains again returned, due to dermatitis. Treatment, however, was continued every other day, tube being placed farther away from affected area, and in about two weeks more a marked change was noticeable. The hollow cavity of the growth seemed to fill in, the edges of the ulcer began to approach one another, and in three months from the beginning of the treatment the wound had healed over entirely, and the patient presented the appearance of having been born with only one breast, so slight was the scar. This patient has been under observation for nearly one year, and during this time no recurrence has been noticed. Patient is a very active woman, and travels extensively.

CASE IV.—Mrs. A., aged sixty-five years, case of lupus involving entire forehead, left temporal region, left cheek and eye, and extending to the middle of the left side of the nose. The most extensive lupus formation we have ever seen. Primary lesion a pimple, which developed on left cheek bone over fifteen years ago, constantly grew larger until thirteen years ago medical aid was sought. Various local preparations were tried without avail. Lupus area became constantly larger, even though patient has been practically under treatment of some kind or other for the past thirteen years. Two years ago plaster treatment was resorted to without any beneficial result, and since then the growth discharged constantly and itched intensely, and patient became very weak, due to constant irritation. X-ray treatment began December 2, 1901, and continued every day until January 10, 1902, at which time the looked-for dermatitis had developed over the entire area, and the patient was allowed to rest from treatment. Three weeks elapsed before the irritation had run its course, and, at that time, all parts were covered with new and healthy skin. A month later the hair again began growing, on head, eyebrows, and eyelashes, and not a vestige of the old trouble can be found.

CASE V.—Mr. P., aged fifty-five years, lupus on left cheek, surface size of twenty-five-cent piece. Ten years ago patient noticed small festering pimple on cheek, which was opened by scratching with the finger nail. This has never healed over in spite of the fact that he has been constantly under treatment, and tried, among other things, the actual cautery three times, excision once, and plaster treatment five times. Patient was sent to us by his son, a physician, and x-ray treatment recommended. Treatment given daily for seven weeks, at which time considerable dermatitis had developed, and patient was allowed to go home, and instructed to return as soon as the irritation, due to the treatment, had subsided. The dermatitis did not subside for nearly three weeks, when patient appeared, and we found a small area in the center of the old formation, which needed treatment. Accordingly, treatments were again given daily for two weeks, when dermatitis once more developed, and patient was again allowed to rest from treatment. On returning two weeks later we were unable to find any trace of the previous trouble, and since that time, now nearly six months, we have seen and examined this patient several times, and have been unable to find any return of the lupus.

CASE VI.—Mrs. F., aged fifty years, large scirrhus on left breast of three years' standing. Had injection treatment without any favorable effect. Would not undergo surgical treatment because she had heard of many recurrences following operation. X-ray treatment undertaken April 15, 1901, daily for first two months, after which decided dermatitis developed, and the breast began to break down, and discharged not only a large quantity of fluid, but also much solid cancer tissue. This breaking-down process continued for over one month when the parts began to heal. The growth seemed to have been entirely enucleated. Treatments were now given every other day, and in the course of two months or more the wound had entirely healed, and, indeed, without much scarring. This patient has been examined frequently, and no return detected.

CASE VII.—Mrs. E., aged fifty-two years. Early in the year 1900 the patient complained of pain in the pelvic region. On consulting several physicians the diagnosis of cancer of the uterus was made and operation was recommended. Operation for removal of entire uterus was performed March, 1900. Following this operation, a persistent discharge was noticed. The patient took a severe cold in the month of December, 1900, and symptoms of congestion appeared in the pelvic region, followed by the development of an abscess, which broke and discharged through the vagina. Discharge continued offensive, with occasional very profuse hemorrhages. A second operation was recommended and performed by a prominent surgeon in May, 1901. On making an incision the surgeon found that the cancer had returned, and was so extensive in character that he decided not to remove anything. The wound was closed, and the husband was told that nothing could be done to save his wife's life, and that she would probably die within a month. During the last week of May, 1901, patient was brought to Chicago, and x-ray treatment was undertaken. Daily treatments of ten minutes' duration were given, and at the end of two months the patient had gained twenty-two pounds, was free from pain, and the foul discharge had almost entirely ceased. At the end of three months she was discharged symptomatically cured, and she remains so to this writing. During the past eleven months she has gained thirty-five pounds, and writes "I continue to keep well; have not felt so well in years."

We have a number of other patients who have taken x-ray treatment, and who have remained free from recurrence for periods ranging from six months to a year and a half. Many other cases could be cited, but time and space forbid.

In conclusion, we wish to submit the following deductions:

1. The x-ray is the most remarkable therapeutic agent of the last decade.

2. In properly selected cases of so-called "incurable conditions" the x-ray has brought about remarkable results.

3. Relief from pain is one of the most prominent features of the treatment.

4. Retrogressive changes are noticed in all primary cancer or tuberculous growths.

5. The x-ray has a pronounced effect upon internal cancers.

6. The greatest value of the x-ray is obtained in treating post-operative cases to prevent recurrences.

7. The proportion of clinical cures by this treatment is greater than that obtainable by any other method of treatment.

8. We are positively justified in assuming an idiosyncrasy to x-rays.

Emil H. Grubbe

9. The peculiarities of each case must be studied in order to get the best results, i. e. no strict rules for treatment can be laid down.

10. Dermatitis, if properly produced, is within certain limits a desirable feature of x-ray treatment.

11. Since the vacuum of an ordinary x-ray tube changes constantly, such tubes are useless for radio-therapeutic work, and only tubes which allow of perfect control of vacuum should be used.

12. The x-ray has a selective influence upon cells of the body; abnormal cells being effected more readily than the normal.

13. Hemorrhages and discharges are decidedly lessened and, ultimately, cease in the majority of cases.

14. Even in the hopeless, inoperable cases, the x-ray prolongs life, makes the patient comfortable, and the last hours free from pain.

The use of the x-ray is, without doubt, a very valuable addition to the therapeutics of malignant diseases, and cannot demand too much attention from the progressive physician.

Whatever may be the real action of the x-ray in these diseases, the results obtained certainly have been astonishing, and while it would be premature to claim that malignant diseases can positively be cured, it is to be hoped that further investigations may surpass our expectations.

TREATMENT OF DYSMENORRHEA WITH FARADIC ELECTRICITY

In presenting this paper, I wish to state that I will not introduce a new remedy. "There is nothing new under the sun"—not even in the field of electricity. The treatment with which my paper deals was originated by Apostoli in 1858—many years ago, you see. I have only modified his method, and wish to re-introduce it with these modifications.

Woman's life, between certain ages, is characterized by menstruation. Menstruation should be a normal function, but, due to occupation, local or constitutional causes, it is more often an anomaly.

Reprinted from *The Clinique*, Vol. XXXIII, No. 1 (January, 1912).

Dysmenorrhea is one of the most common, if not the most common, menstrual disorder brought to our notice, and although not a disease *per se*, it is a symptom of such importance that treatment is demanded. So much has been said and written about dysmenorrhea and its treatment that it would seem every one must have full knowledge of the subject, and therefore every case could be helped as soon as discovered. Not so, however. It is a well known fact that the remedies ordinarily employed for the relief of this trouble are either inefficient or else are of a character more to be dreaded than poison.

The usual routine treatments, consisting of douches, tampons, hip and foot baths, hypnotic drugs, or the replacing of the uterus, if displaced, by pessaries, are, at best, most crude and ineffective measures. They all fall short of the ideal treatment. It is true that surgery can be offered to some, but when the patient will not submit to an operation, what then? Furthermore, there is, from a scientific standpoint, considerable doubt as to the ultimate value of surgery in this trouble. True, surgery can make the uterine canal larger in caliber, but is that all that is required? Will heroic dilation of the canal cure the case? I think I am not far from the truth when I say it seldom cures. What is wrong? Well, simply this: Dilating the uterine canal forcibly will not permanently influence the nutrition, the growth or function of the uterus and its appendages, and therefore should not be expected to be curative. If we wish to cure these cases we must resort to remedies which will develop the muscular fibers of the uterus, and cause the organ not only to increase its function, but also its anatomy. In other words, let us use common sense instead of heroic sense. Surgical dilation merely aims at one single symptom, rather than at the cause of the trouble, and therefore is not very logical treatment, to say the least.

About the kinds and causes of dysmenorrhea, much might be said. The books speak of mechanical dysmenorrhea, congestive or inflammatory dysmenorrhea, neuralgic dysmenorrhea, virginal dysmenorrhea, etc. When we remember that what is called dysmenorrhea is only a symptom, it will appear somewhat presumptuous to treat it as a disease.

My personal opinion as regards the probable cause of most dysmenorrheas is that an endometritis, which has become chronic, causes a spasm of the internal os of the uterus. This spasmodic condition is especially active when the uterus is engorged with blood, as is the case just before and during a menstrual period.

Very naturally on first thought one would blame most of these troubles to a stenosis of the uterine canal, or an atrophy or lack of development of the muscular or mucous tissues of the uterus, but these are not nearly so often the cause of painful menstruation as is the spasmodic condition above referred to.

Serious study of the different varieties of dysmenorrhea brings one to the conclusion that in the final analysis all cases have a mechanical origin, and also in the majority of subjects the cause will be found in the uterus itself. In other words, our attention should be given locally —to the uterus.

Most physicians, when treating dysmenorrhea, restrict themselves to the use of internal or local remedies, which are palliative but not curative. Let us look at this matter rationally. What are the objects to be attained in treating dysmenorrhea? Relief from pain? Yes. Not only relief from pain, but removal of the cause of pain, so that future periods will be free from trouble. As stated before, the largely mechanical origin of this condition should direct us to the organ most concerned. Not only that; if the causes of dysmenorrhea are mechanical, the probability is that mechanical remedies might be useful. Since the trouble is due largely to lack of functional activity in all the structures composing the uterus, the necessity for treatment which can increase this activity is self-evident.

In this day of competition between therapeutic measures, it might be well to go back occasionally to see if we have not missed something. I wish to call attention to an old remedy; a remedy as old as the proverbial hills; a natural remedy. I refer to exercise; exercise of muscular tissue for the purpose of developing function and growth. You will agree that since dysmenorrhea is such a common and nerve-racking condition, no remedy should be slighted which offers a ray of hope.

Electricity has always occupied a prominent place in the armamentarium of the gynecologist, and in the treatment of dysmenorrhea it is one of the most valuable remedies at our command. It is well established that faradic electricity can be utilized to exercise and develop muscular tissue. For many years this current has been employed and considered of greatest value in the treatment of muscular atrophy. Just as you see the biceps muscle of the arm dilate and contract under the influence of faradic electricity, so any other muscle of the body may be made to react. This is a fact which cannot be controverted. The effect of this current is similar to that obtained from the normal use of dumb-bell or Indian club exercise. In this way we can give muscular tissue a course of gymnastics. The principles of developing and strengthening tissues by working them systematically are today so well understood and valued that no champion is needed.

The uterus is a muscular organ. By means of suitable electrodes, faradic electricity can be localized in this organ. Therefore, we can secure the beneficial effects of the muscle developing qualities of this current in the uterus just as we do in paralysis or any other condition in which the muscular function is not up to par. Furthermore, this is not only a natural therapeutic agent, but there is also this advantage— it acts in a way which is perfectly natural to the tissues. Since no chemical action is established during the application, it follows that no harm can result from even an overdose.

The rhythmic dilating and contracting effects of the current cause the uterus and its neighboring parts to develop so that there is healthy action; the expulsive power of the organ is increased, and when future periods arrive the blood is expelled more readily, and consequently the pains vanish. This sedative action is marked, some patients reporting freedom from pain after the first application. By this means, also, the circulation in the uterine blood vessels can be excited and toned up, with a consequent increase in the nutrition of the organ. Then, too, the uterine ligaments are also acted upon. If relaxed, they are shortened, which tends to correct flexions and versions, and therefore the uterus is replaced to a more normal position in the pelvis.

Furthermore, the muscular parts of the vagina also become indirectly influenced by the current, and any relation here is corrected and a tendency to the normal again established.

In short, without taxing or harming the tissues in the least, this treatment helps the muscular, circulatory and nervous functions of the uterus and neighboring parts to normal physiological action. This is not theory but fact, and there is nothing empiric about it. It must be obvious to any practitioner that this treatment is logical and beneficial, and therefore presents very definite points of merit.

The current used in this treatment is the faradic—the induction coil current. After generation, it is run through a mechanical rheotome which is arranged to interrupt 20 times per minute. To control the amount of electricity, I use a rheostat of graphite, with a measuring dial attached. With this arrangement (which is a device of my own) the current strength can be very accurately gauged.

The treatment may be given in several ways and good results obtained. Two methods which I prefer may be called, for sake of distinction, the intra-uterine and the extra-uterine methods. In the intra-uterine method a bi-polar electrode having two rings of metal separated by insulating material is made of suitable size to fit the os uteri. After this electrode is introduced into the uterus, both poles of the electrical circuit are attached, one each to one of the rings on the electrode, and all the current is concentrated in the uterus.

In the extra-uterine method an electrode of such size and shape is used as will readily pass through the vaginal opening and yet give large surface contact when it touches the uterus. This electrode constitutes the active part of the circuit. The other pole of the current is attached to a rectal electrode, which is so made that insulation is obtained everywhere except where it touches the bowel opposite the uterus.

The technique of this treatment is not very difficult. With the proper kind of apparatus, and with care in its use, no unusual amount of skill is required.

In using the intra-uterine method the patient is put on a table, lying on the back, with the knees elevated. A vaginal speculum is used, and the vagina and uterus are swabbed as thoroughly as possible with a 5% solution of permanganate of potash. Then the bi-polar electrode, previously sterilized and warmed, is slowly and gently passed into the uterus until both of the metal rings disappear into the cavity. Next the rheotome, or interrupter, is started. Finally the current is turned on and increased very gradually by moving the handle of the rheostat or controller around until the patient feels the contractions quite plainly. In determining the dosage the patient's individual needs and tolerance are to be considered. An infantile uterus will not need as much current as a subinvoluted and displaced one. Good, full and vigorous contractions should be produced. However, too strong currents should not be used, even though the patient may say she can take them. Mild stimulation obtained from comparatively weak currents produce muscle contractions of greatest value.

Although ordinary manipulation of the electrodes does no harm to the endometrium, the importance of exercising the utmost care and gentleness in giving each treatment cannot be dwelt upon too much. Never introduce the electrode unwarmed, and never use pressure such that bleeding at the os results. Never remove the electrodes before the current has been shut off, and never suddenly shut the electricity off at its source; always turn it off gradually by means of the rheostat. Make sure that the circuit is not "alive" before disconnecting the patient. The removal of the instruments should be done with the same gentleness and care as their introduction.

Where the treatment per os uteri is impracticable, as in virgins, the extra-uterine method is used. The patient is told that the bowels should be thoroughly moved, preferably flushed, immediately before each treatment. With the body on the table, lying on the back, and the knees elevated, the active electrode is introduced into the vagina and carried down so that it makes contact with the uterus. This electrode is attached to one pole of the circuit. The other electrode is introduced into the rectum and attached to the other pole. Next the mechanical interrupter is started, and then the electricity is switched on. Finally the rheostat is used to turn on the desired amount of current.

To make the electrodes pass readily, they should be lubricated with sterile glycerine, or a tragacanth mixture. Vaseline or other oily lubricants should never be used, as they offer too much resistance and therefore prevent the electricity from entering the body. Each seance should last from 8 to 10 minutes.

Some patients who are very susceptible and nervous complain of cramping, bearing-down pain during the treatment. This uncomfortable feeling, however, does not last long, and always passes away as soon as the sitting is over. On the other hand, the bulk of patients state that the treatment is pleasant, and they feel an immediate beneficial effect following each seance.

It is to be remembered that in order to make the effects of the current lasting repeated treatments are necessary. Just as an occasional use of dumb-bells would not develop any resistance in the muscles of the hand or arm, so an occasional treatment of the uterus by this method will accomplish only temporary results.

I have found every-other-day treatments between the periods to give best results. The patient should be told in advance that, due to the nature of the trouble, and also because of the physiological nature of the treatment, some time should be given in order that a cure may be brought about. It generally requires from 2 to 6 months time for the average case. But not infrequently results may be obtained in a much shorter time.

The following four cases, each one typical, illustrate the value of this method:

CASE I—INFLAMMATORY (CONGESTIVE) DYSMENORRHEA

Mrs. M., age 30. Four years ago, immediately following the birth of her only child, she noticed a discharge, which lasted several months. When she began menstruating again there developed dragging pains in the pelvis. She became extremely nervous; had headaches and nausea. Remained in bed during every period. Her physician diagnosed the trouble congestive dysmenorrhea and treated her for several months, but without avail. She was finally referred to me for electrical treatment. The case showed a gradual beneficial effect after one month's treatment, and was cured in four months. She has not had a painful menstruation now for over a year.

CASE II—NEURALGIC DYSMENORRHEA

Miss B., age 34. Twelve years ago she contracted a severe cold while menstruating, and since then she has had most excruciating pains during each period. Is confined to bed at least three days each month. Pains are at times so bad that hypnotic drugs must be used. Is despondent and hysterical, because her physicians have told her that since they have tried many remedies without getting permanent relief, her trouble can not be cured. As a last resort electricity was tried. At first, due to the hysterical condition, she was a most difficult patient to handle, but after two months' treatment there was so much improvement that she decided to go on. Improvement continued without interruption until she considered herself well. Altogether she was under treatment about six months.

CASE III—OBSTRUCTIVE DYSMENORRHEA

Mrs. S., age 28. Married six years, but never pregnant. When 20 years old was in a railway accident and received internal injuries, following which she developed painful menstruation. Pains in back, hips and pelvis are most agonizing, and start fully two days before the flow begins. Flow is scanty, thick, and almost black in color. Feels exhausted most of the time. Tried many remedies, but nothing seemed to help. Examination revealed decided retroflexion. Under electrical treatment her disagreeable symptoms slowly but surely faded away, and after eight months' steady use of the current she was well. The most remarkable thing to her was the fact that six months after she considered herself cured she became pregnant.

CASE IV—VIRGINAL DYSMENORRHEA (DUE TO LACK OF DEVELOPMENT OF THE UTERUS)

Miss H., age 17. High school girl. Began menstruating at fourteen. Flow is irregular and scanty, amounting to only a few drops. Pain in pelvis and back is so severe that she must remain home several days during each period. Her complexion is pallid, she is morose and has lost interest in her studies. Was told that a surgical operation would possibly help, but both she and the parents refused this remedy. They finally decided to try electricity. She received 14 treatments before a period appeared. Although she had some pains during the whole period, they were as nothing compared with her previous troubles, for this was the first period she ever spent out of bed. Gradually she improved in general. The pains became less and less at each succeeding period, and the flow also became more profuse and regular. After about six months' treatment she was pronounced cured. Two years have elapsed since.

Here I wish to express the opinion that sterility is most often due to lack of development of the uterus. Also that dysmenorrhea in virgins is most often due to the same condition. I am also convinced that if this treatment is begun early enough and properly carried out, the majority of cases of infantile uterus can be developed and cured.

Summing up my experience with this treatment, I can say:

It offers to woman freedom from a very common and usually unnecessary complaint.

It is a safe and logical method, which cannot be said of most other treatments used for this trouble.

Theoretically, at least, this treatment ought to appeal to all who give the matter serious thought.

Practically, the results are almost ideal.

It is useful in all forms of dysmenorrhea, and, although a very effective treatment, produces no objectional by or after effects.

It rests upon broad scientific principles, and, when generally understood, will not only find a permanent place in the therapeutics of dysmenorrhea, but will also displace other less active measures.

I do not wish to imply that with the re-introduction of this method the millennium in the treatment of dysmenorrhea has arrived, but when positive, permanent, and almost immediate results follow the use of a remedy one can become almost enthusiastic.

One Hundred and Thirty-Nine Cases of Skin Cancer Cured by X-Rays

The use of x-rays in the treatment of skin cancer dates back to 1896, when Dr. John E. Gilman, of Chicago, first suggested that this newly discovered agent might offer possibilities in the treatment of malignant conditions.

Even at that early date, with most imperfect and comparatively inefficient apparatus, almost magical results were obtained in a number of cases. It was but natural that these striking results should create enthusiasts whose language pertaining to the value of this treatment appeared to know no bounds. However, I need hardly state that even the wildest dreams of the pioneers have been realized, for the x-ray has gradually extended its sphere of usefulness until, at the present time, it occupies a unique position in therapeutics. Some therapeutic agents come, are used for a short time and then are laid aside for other more potent measures, but the x-ray has, during a period of nearly twenty years, become more and more useful as its peculiar properties have been studied, and to-day it ranks as the remedy of choice in quite a list of pathological conditions. X-ray therapy then is no longer in the experimental stage. The vast amount of literature bearing upon this subject is an appreciation of its importance.

It is a matter of history that I took a conspicuous part in the birth and development of x-ray therapy, and as I have been intimately connected with this phase of work ever since, I feel that I have had exceptional opportunities for observation and experience.

In previous papers dealing with this subject I have discussed the value of x-ray treatment as an adjunct to other treatment. In this paper, although I have had under observation nearly 500 cases of skin and mucous membrane cancer, I shall confine myself to the consideration of 155 cases of this disease under x-ray treatment, exclusively.

In order that a fair estimate of a remedy may be formed, selected cases only should be treated.

In skin cancer selected or ideal cases are not those in which metastases are present. I am of the opinion that when cancer involves the glandular system, then the case is not curable by any method of treatment known to-day, surgery not excepted. In epitheliomata of mucous surfaces the depth of tissue involved determines whether the case is

Reprinted from the *Interstate Medical Journal*, Vol. XXIII, No. 10, (St. Louis, 1916).

ideal for x-ray treatment or not. So long as the mucous membrane alone is affected x-rays will produce good results but, if the disease has extended to the submucous structures, then the case is not an ideal one for this treatment.

Carcinoma of the skin probably never occurs as a primary lesion but is secondary and due to migration of cancer cells from some other part of the body to the epidermis. This particular form of cancer, therefore, is not very amenable to x-ray treatment or any other treatment; consequently I do not classify such cases as ideal for this method.

Whether the case be ideal or not, doubt need seldom be expressed concerning the diagnosis of skin cancer. Most cases come to us in the ulcerated stage. With cocaine and the curette we can readily remove enough material so that a microscopical examination is possible. However, a word of caution should be given here to the effect that extensive curettage is a dangerous procedure because it opens up channels for the spread of cancer cells. The curette should therefore not be used too extensively.

Practically all the cases reported in this paper have been microscoped by competent laboratories. I have done this not so much to be able to controvert those who are loath to acknowledge the correctness of the diagnosis when cancer has disappeared and remained absent for some time following x-ray treatment, but to convince myself of the possibilities and limitations of this treatment; in other words, to establish its true position in electro therapeutics.

The action of x-rays on cancer tissue has been studied by a large number of investigators, and the consensus of opinion is that heroic cumulative effects of x-rays produce primarily a gradual atrophy of the cancer cells and later a granular degeneration and absorption of these cells. At the same time a proportionate stimulation of connective-tissue cell formation is noticed. These new connective-tissue cells ultimately occupy the place left vacant by the destroyed cancer cells.

"Practice makes perfect." This is particularly true of the application of x-rays in skin cancer. In the early days we gave comparatively small doses of the rays and produced proportionately small results. Now we give larger doses and get in return much better and quicker results. Like all other therapeutic agents the x-ray possesses dual action. Weak doses produce physiologic effects, while large doses produce toxic effects.

In the treatment of skin cancer too small doses of x-rays are harmful because they stimulate the cancerous growth to greater activity. This fact should be kept constantly before us. Half-way measures should not be used when heroic measures are in order. The treatment of epithelial cancers should be essentially destructive, and for that reason massive applications of the rays should always be given.

There is no doubt in my mind that the more vigorous the treatment the more favorable will be the prognosis. Therefore, all cancers should be treated with the least possible delay. The massive dose or the "intensive method of treatment" gains time more than anything else and should appeal to us for that reason particularly, but it also produces the same decided distinctive effects in the cancer cells which would be produced by the slower technique.

To make sure that all active cancer cells will be destroyed I always expose a small area of healthy tissue just outside the limits of the cancer lesion, to the action of the x-ray. If any cancer cells have extended out into this apparently healthy region they will be destroyed at the same time that the major malignant tissue is affected. In treating thus there is little likelihood of a recurrence. Such application of the x-ray is analogous to the wide excision or dissection practised by the surgeon when the knife is used in treating cancer.

I maintain that it is essential to produce a decided inflammatory reaction or dermatitis in these cases in order to secure the best effects. The usual reaction is ushered in with a pronounced erythema, then come swelling, tanning, itching, erosion and finally considerable soreness. I consider a fairly severe reaction desirable because more permanent results can be expected therefrom. A mild reaction may result in healing over the ulcer, but a recurrence of the cancer is very apt to take place. If the newly formed scar tissue be weak and slow in becoming hardened, it is an indication that more vigorous x-ray treatment must be resorted to in order to clear up the case.

I have been able to cure cases of skin cancer with high vacuum as well as low vacuum tubes, but since it is not advisable unnecessarily to affect healthy tissues beneath the lesion, and since practically no penetration of the ray in these cases is required, I prefer a low or soft tube; as a rule a 1-3-inch air resisting vacuum is best. If the high vacuum tube is used, an aluminum screen at least one millimeter in thickness should be placed between the lesion and the x-ray tube. Ordinarily much more rapid cumulative effects can be obtained with the unfiltered rays because the alpha and beta rays which are then active on the lesion produce cumulative effects in one-eighth the time required for filtered gamma rays.

The advent of the Coolidge tube has made it possible to control x-rays absolutely. But even though it has simplified x-ray therapy considerably I do not consider this tube essential in treating skin cancers. Although I have often cured cases of skin cancer with a single massive dose, I do not wish to convey the idea that intensive x-ray treatment necessarily means treatment with a Coolidge tube, neither does it mean one single application with an ordinary tube. Under certain circumstances the dose may be given in divided amounts, *i. e.*, at several sittings. Now, more than in the past the use of x-rays therapeutically requires discrimination, skill and judgment, which makes it almost impossible for the tyro who is usually superficial and a hopeless routinist to dabble with successfully.

The total number of uncomplicated skin cancers which I have treated with x-rays *exclusively* is 155.

In order that my results may be compared with other treatments, I append a table showing the time following discharge of the patient during which no recurrence has appeared.

> 2 have remained free from recurrence fourteen years.
> 2 have remained free from recurrence thirteen years.
> 3 have remained free from recurrence twelve years.
> 2 have remained free from recurrence eleven years.
> 3 have remained free from recurrence ten years.
> 4 have remained free from recurrence nine years.
> 3 have remained free from recurrence eight years.
> 6 have remained free from recurrence seven years.
> 8 have remained free from recurrence six years.
> 14 have remained free from recurrence five years.
> 20 have remained free from recurrence four years.
> 20 have remained free from recurrence three years.
> 25 have remained free from recurrence two years.
> 27 have remained free from recurrence one year.

A total of 139 cases have remained free from recurrence for more than one year.

In some of the remaining 16 cases I have not been able to get a subsequent history; some have died from intercurrent disease or accident.

Sufficient time has elapsed in a large enough number of the cases to enable us to draw conclusions as to the ultimate results obtained. Omitting those cases which have not yet remained well more than three years, the balance of my list makes a very good showing and proves this treatment well adapted to skin cancer.

If we consider, for the sake of argument, that the 16 cases which are not accounted for are failures, we still have over 90 per cent of the total number of cases treated to classify as clinically cured. I am convinced that with better technique and conservative selection of cases even a much larger percentage of cures can be produced.

As more direct evidence of the efficiency of exclusive x-ray treatment in skin cancer I will add the abridged histories of just a few typical cases.

CASE I.—Mr. J. H., æt. forty-five, sent by Dr. W. J. Truitt. This was a case of ulcerative or basal-celled epithelioma of the right cheek on line with the mouth, area of ulcer the size of a five cent piece. Received altogether 15 divided dose treatments. Patient was discharged symptomatically cured September 30th, 1906, and has remained free from recurrence.

CASE II.—Mrs. J. B. C., æt. thirty-five, sent by Dr. J. E. Gilman.

Diagnosis Paget's disease of the left breast. This case was treated in the early period of x-ray work and therefore received a large number of treatments before a cumulative effect was produced. Following this the lesion healed and remained well about one year, when it recurred. However, the patient was not discouraged and concluded that the remedy which once controlled the situation would prove effective again. Accordingly she returned for another series of treatments, and the ulcer was again healed and has remained so since April, 1906.

CASE III.—Mr. J. B., æt. sixty, sent by Dr. G. M. Hill. This was a case of granulomatous type of epithelioma on the lower lip, a so-called smoker's cancer. The patient received 10 full dose treatments when a decided reaction occurred. Following subsidence of x-ray irritation the ulcer healed and has remained well nine years.

CASE IV.—Mrs. L. J. K., æt. forty, sent by Dr. Leroy Thompson. Diagnosis round-celled sarcoma on right side of nose near region of tear-duct. This case was operated surgically and although a wide, clean excision was made the disease reappeared immediately and was growing rapidly when the patient was sent to me for x-ray treatment. Although the prognosis was not favorable, yet with heroic doses of the x-ray the value of this treatment was most strikingly demonstrated, for she was cured and is perfectly well to-day.

CASE V.—Mr. A. T., æt. sixty-five, sent by Dr. M. C. Bragdon, diagnosis nodular type of epithelioma on back of right hand, lesion the size of a quarter. This case was treated by the divided dose technique and consequently required 21 separate applications before a cure resulted.

CASE VI.—Mr. M. H. McG., æt. sixty, sent by Dr. F. McNamara, diagnosed as squamous celled type of epithelioma involving the middle of the lower lip. Ulcer the size of a dime. Received 5 heroic doses of the x-ray. Eventually, after the reaction subsided, the parts healed beautifully and hardly any scar is now visible.

CASE VII.—Mrs. M. K., æt. forty, sent by Dr. J. Delprat, diagnosis semi-fibroid type of epithelioma involving whole of upper lip and lower one-half of the nose with extensive destruction of the septum. This case had previously been treated with arsenic paste, followed by surgical excision but without benefit. Previous to her visit to me she had also received several x-ray applications at the hands of another operator, but undoubtedly they were too mild for no reaction had occurred. After I gave her 6 massive doses of x-rays, such decided sloughing of the ulcerated area was produced that it became completely enucleated. The wound healed perfectly and there has been no recurrence in more than six years.

This case is mentioned to impress the importance of pushing x-ray treatment when once begun until a cumulative effect is produced. The line between success and failure is so fine that we are often right on the line but do not know it. If the operator had pushed his treatment a little more or impressed the patient with more confidence in his ability to produce results if the treatments were continued, undoubtedly success would have been achieved earlier. Success, therefore, depends not only upon selection of the proper remedy but also upon the proper manipulation of that remedy.

I believe we are justified in saying that those who are clinically or symptomatically cured by x-ray treatment are less likely to have a recurrence than those who have received other treatment. If to this we add the fact that x-ray treatment is a bloodless treatment; that no blood-vessels are opened up for the possible spread of cancer cells to other parts of the body; that it is a simple, safe, painless, non-confining and non-disfiguring treatment, then surely the burden should be upon the other methods to show cause why x-rays should not be used in every case of uncomplicated skin cancer.

Priority in the Therapeutic Use of X-Rays

In order that the history of x-rays may properly record events in the order in which they occurred, and also for the purpose of giving credit where credit is due, I submit the following brief.

Recently, while looking through some boxes which contained records of the happenings of many years ago, I discovered several references (which I thought had long been destroyed by fire) pertaining to my own early work in the x-ray field. Under the light of this newly found material, I feel that the claims, which have been made for others, to priority in the therapeutic use of x-rays, should no longer go unchallenged by me.

In other words, when my records are compared with all the available records of others in this field, I am convinced that the way will have been opened for me to make the following claims:

First, that I was the first person exposed to x-rays who received sufficient cumulative effects to develop x-ray dermatitis.

Second, that I was the first person to apply x-rays to pathologic lesions on living human subjects for therapeutic purposes.

Third, that I was the first to use sheet lead, or, for that matter, any other substance, as a protective against untoward x-ray effects.

The evidence which I am able to bring out of the seclusion of nearly

Reprinted from *Radiology*, XXI (August, 1933), 136.

thirty-nine years, and which constitutes the bases of my claims, comprises—

First, a business card of mine of the year 1895, which shows that, at the time the discovery of the x-ray was announced, I was a manufacturer of vacuum tubes; and

Second, two introductory letters, written by the two physicians who sent the first two patients to me for x-ray treatment.

Although I have had frequent occasions to refer to this pioneering effort of mine (having been, from the beginning, a teacher of roentgenology and also having written many monographs dealing practically with all the different phases of x-ray work), I am frank when I state that I never have made a campaign to have my claims to priority in the therapeutic use of x-rays officially, as it were, accepted.

I must state in passing that, at the time I did this work, I could not realize the importance of the subject, nor how involved with controversy it would become in later years. As mentioned before, I believed that all written evidence bearing upon this issue had been destroyed by fire. This, together with the fact that, with the exception of myself, all those directly connected with this event had died before this subject had reached the controversial stage, would make it doubly difficult, if not impossible, for me to substantiate my claims. I felt that circumstances were against me, and, without the evidence which I now have in my possession, the channels of credit were closed to me, and that I could not, therefore, expect support for my claims.

But now, after nearly four decades of waiting, I am in a position to assert my claims for recognition in this particular field, and, I hope, to receive the credit, which, I feel, should have been mine all these years.

To briefly review matters, during the latter part of October, 1895, Prof. William Roentgen began the serious study of cathode rays. While duplicating some experiments of Prof. P. Lenard (also of Germany), relative to fluorescence produced in chemicals when exposed to the cathode ray, Roentgen discovered that barium-platinum-cyanide crystals fluoresced with the greatest volume of light. He also found, as Lenard had discovered, that light-sensitive chemicals, such as photographic papers and plates, were affected by exposure to the rays which emanated from the vacuum tube. On November 8, 1895, Roentgen wrote the first announcement of this work to the Physical Institute of the University of Würtzburg, Germany. His next, and most startling, announcement, was made before the Physio-medical Society of Würtzburg, on December 28th of the same year.

Incidentally, I might say that, to scientists who had been working with vacuum phenomena, the discovery of Roentgen was not nearly so startling as it was to the layman. Many commentators on this subject state that the discovery of Roentgen burst upon the world without the least warning. This may have appeared so to the general public, but so far as pure science was concerned, it was positively not so.

In order that the subject, as a whole, may be more clearly understood, it seems to me that a brief account of the work which led up to Roentgen's discovery may not be out of order.

We must go back to the year 1859, when Plücker, of Germany, first recorded the fact that, after a vacuum tube had been frequently excited with high voltage current, an apple-green fluorescence was observable on the inner wall of the tube.

In the year 1860, Prof. Hittorf showed that the luminous stream in an electrically excited vacuum tube could be deflected by a magnet.

In 1875, Sir William Crookes made his first high vacuum tube and discovered that the apple-green light of Plücker had its origin at the negative end of the tube. Crookes therefore called this phenomenon the cathode ray.

Crookes, in 1879, was the first to suggest the concave shape of the cathode electrode, in order that it might bring the cathode stream to a focus. Somehow, no practical use of this idea was made until 1893, when Prof. Herbert Jackson revived it by placing the anode of the tube in such a position that it would catch the cathode stream where the rays came to a focal point.

In 1894 Jackson added to this improvement, by placing the anode at an angle of about sixty degrees, in order to reflect the cathode rays out of the tube.

In the latter part of 1892 and early in 1893, Prof. H. Hertz discovered that cathode (?) rays would pass through cloth, paper, wood, gold foil, and thin aluminum sheets when these substances were placed in the path of the rays.

In December, 1893, Prof. P. Lenard made a Crookes tube with a window of aluminum in it. Through this window he conveyed the cathode (?) rays out of the vacuum of the tube into the air. Also, in August, 1895, he listed a number of substances capable of fluorescing when placed in the path of the cathode (?) rays. In September, 1895, he reported that he had sent the cathode (?) rays through his own hand, and even then (after passing through his hand) these rays excited chemicals to fluorescence. Also, in October, 1895, he reported that he had observed that light-sensitive chemicals, *i.e.*, photographic materials, were affected by exposure to cathode (?) rays.

From the foregoing we will have to conclude that Lenard was really working with x-rays most of the years 1894 and 1895, but, of course, he did not know that. We will also have to conclude that every experimenter who sent a high tension current through a Crookes tube, obtained not only cathode rays, but also x-rays.

Roentgen, in duplicating Lenard's experiments, did something which the latter had not done. First, he covered the Crookes tube with a cardboard box; next he darkened the room in which the experiment was performed; then he sent the electric current through the tube, and finally, he placed his hand between the fluorescent chemical and the

Crookes tube, and when the crystals of barium-platinum-cyanide began to glow, he saw the shadow outlines of the bones of his hand.

All whose names I have mentioned in the preceding paragraphs, and many others, including myself, who had experimented with high vacuum tubes undoubtedly had x-rays every time the "apple-green light" of Plücker was present in their electrically excited Crookes tubes.

The point I am trying to make is, that x-rays were in existence before Roentgen discovered them. Yes, we really had x-rays in the year 1859—thirty-six years before Roentgen announced the finding of them. So it must be evident that, to those conversant with vacuum phenomena, the discovery of Roentgen was not so startling after all. The truth is, that the labors of Lenard had prepared them to expect just about what Roentgen found. On January 4, 1896, Roentgen went to Berlin and again presented his paper. Following this lecture the public press heralded his discovery to all the world.

At the very time when Roentgen did this work I also was working with Crookes tubes, studying the fluorescence of chemicals. I had read in "Annalen der Physik und Chemie," of September and October, 1895, of the experiments of Lenard, and I was duplicating this work when the discovery of x-rays was announced by Roentgen. Under the stimulus of this new discovery I worked almost continuously for several days, duplicating Roentgen's experiments and making new Crookes tubes. I was, in all probability, one of the earliest experimenters with the new rays. The subject was of particular interest to me, because, at that time, I was not only an experimenter with vacuum tubes but also a manufacturer of these devices. My business card of that period read:

E. H. GRUBBÉ
Assayer and Refiner of Rare Metals
Manufacturer of
Incandescent Lamps, Geissler and Crookes Tubes
12 Pacific Avenue   Chicago

Naturally, then, my interest in and appreciation of Roentgen's discovery were pronounced. I should also state that I was one of the very few who had available all the apparatus needed to duplicate the experiments which led up to the discovery of x-rays. I did not have to go out and purchase or have made any part of the equipment. With the exception of photographic plates, I had everything—Crookes tubes, induction coil, electric current generators, fluorescent chemicals—right at hand. Not only that, but, being a chemist and physicist, I was one of the few who had technical knowledge sufficient to appreciate the importance of this discovery. Then, too, I needed no one to teach me the use of these devices.

For the purpose of exciting my home-made Crookes tubes I used the secondary current of a home-made Ruhmkorff induction coil. It is interesting to note here that I also used a home-made static generator as an exciter. However, I found this machine too lacking in current output, when compared with the induction coil. Nevertheless, at the beginning of April, 1896, in conjunction with C. S. Neiswanger, I did considerable research work with larger static generators, at the factory of the McIntosh Battery and Optical Company of Chicago. These larger machines were found quite capable of exciting the Crookes tubes for practical purposes.

As a manufacturer of vacuum tubes I made it a point to know what others were doing in this line. I was, of course, familiar with the research which had been carried on in the vacuum field by such men as Geissler, Sprengel, Toepler, Nobel, Shentone, Silvanus Thompson, Weinhold, and Kahlbaum.

The first Crookes tubes I worked with did not have a large output of x-ray energy. I judged that this was due to the fact that the cathode rays in my tubes were not concentrated sufficiently to transform them into effective x-ray value. Then I recalled having read that Jackson had in the two previous years improved the Crookes tube by decidedly cup-shaping the cathode. With this improvement the cathode stream could be brought to a focus. Also, in order to prevent the enormously high temperature which was generated where this focal area occurred, from melting or puncturing the glass wall of the tube, an anode of platinum was placed in such a position that it would intercept the cathode rays, thus keeping the heat from the glass; in addition, this anode was placed at an angle of sixty degrees in order that it might reflect the cathode rays out of the tube. Theoretically, this offered a decided improvement over the old-style Crookes tube. I immediately made a tube embodying the ideas of Jackson. The very first tube I made after this pattern was much more efficient than any I had tried before, and so, thereafter, I used only this type of Crookes tube for all my work.

Undoubtedly it was because of my early use of this method of focusing or concentration of the cathode ray on the anode of the tube that I developed x-ray dermatitis very shortly.

Incidentally, it must be remembered that, having worked with Crookes tubes in the study of fluorescence before December 28, 1895, my body had been exposed to x-rays some time before Roentgen made his announcement.

I made a number of tubes, all of which I tested for vacuum by exposing my left hand between the tubes and fluorescent materials. This was done many times daily for many days. In other words, my left hand was practically touching the excited Crookes tubes during most of the testing periods. These frequent and long exposures to the x-ray produced a cumulative effect, so that, by the beginning of the last week of January, 1896, I had developed a dermatitis on the back of my left hand, which was so acute that I sought medical aid.

At first my symptoms were erythema, edema, hyperemia, and hyperesthesia. A few days later there was bleb and blister formation, with skin desquamation and epilation of the hair. Later the skin cracked and ulcers formed. (Parenthetically I would state that this hand was amputated piecemeal, and for some years it has been gone entirely.)

On January 27, 1896, I consulted my attending physician, Dr. J. P. Cobb, in the faculty room of the Hahnemann Medical College (which later became the General Medical College). Dr. Cobb was a professor, and I an undergraduate medical student, in this institution. While Dr. Cobb was examining my hand, Dr. J. E. Gilman, Dr. A. C. Halphide, and Dr. R. Ludlam, all of them professors in the college, entered the room. My ailment being a new one, Dr. Cobb used me as a clinical subject. He explained my symptoms, also the cause, and asked for advice. Each of the doctors present, except Dr. Gilman, offered remedial suggestions. Dr. Gilman, after thinking over the origin of the dermatitis, said that although he would not offer a remedy for the trouble he thought that "any physical agent capable of doing so much damage to normal cells and tissues might offer possibilities, if used as a therapeutic agent, in the treatment of pathologic conditions in which pronounced irritative, blistering, or even destructive effects might be desirable." As examples of such lesions he mentioned cancer, lupus, and indolent ulcer.

This statement of Dr. Gilman's made a profound impression upon all those present, Dr. Ludlam and Dr. Halphide being especially impressed. Both were anxious to know what would happen if pathologic tissues could be exposed to x-rays long enough to get a cumulative effect. Dr. Ludlam said that he had a patient with an open inoperable carcinoma of the left breast, in which there was not only glandular involvement, but also systemic carcinosis. Evidently, this patient was doomed to early death, but he thought the case a good one on which to make a clinical application of Dr. Gilman's idea. If agreeable to me, he would advise this patient to come to me for x-ray treatment. Surely, the treatment could not make her condition more serious; on the other hand, it might be of some benefit. I agreed to accept this patient, if she cared to come for the new treatment.

Dr. Halphide mentioned that he too had a patient who might be induced to try the x-ray treatment. The case was that of a man who had ulcerative lupus vulgaris involving the entire right cheek and extending down into the right side of the neck. I agreed to accept this case also, for x-ray treatment.

On January 29, 1896, Dr. Ludlam's patient arrived at my place of business with the following note:

E. H. Grubbé
    12 Pacific Avenue
Dear Sir:
    This will introduce Mrs. Rose Lee, who has carcinoma of the left breast.

She is willing to have you make x-ray applications.
I hope you can help her.

Yours truly,
R. Ludlam, M.D.

January 28, 1896.

And so, without the blaring of trumpets or the beating of drums, x-ray therapy was born. The very first application of the x-ray for therapeutic purposes was made upon Mrs. Rose Lee's cancerous left breast, by myself. This occurred on January 29, 1896, in Chicago.

The next day, January 30, 1896, Dr. Halphide's patient with lupus vulgaris came to me with a note which read:

E. H. Grubbé
12 Pacific Avenue

Chicago, Jan. 29/96

My dear Sir:
The bearer, Mr. A. Carr, is the patient of whom I spoke the other day. He has had lupus for twelve years. He will come for x-ray treatments as often as you think necessary.

Yours truly,
Dr. A. C. Halphide.

Of course, I had no preconceived technic or method of treatment to use on these two patients, the first to receive x-rays therapeutically. In each case I placed the Crookes tube almost in contact with the lesion. I gave each patient an exposure of about one hour a day. Remembering my dermatitis, I protected the healthy parts of the patient's body, adjacent to the pathologic area, with sheet lead taken from Chinese tea chests.

I believe that this was the first time that sheet lead, or any other substance, was used as a protective against untoward x-ray effects.

Little did I realize, at the time I gave Mrs. Lee her first x-ray treatment, that I was blazing a new trail in the therapeutic field; little did I realize that this was the beginning of a new epoch in the history of medicine.

In spite of the long period of time that has elapsed since my first introduction to this subject, I can recall very vividly the effect which the treating of these, my first patients, had upon me. They were not reported clinically by the physicians who sent them to me for the reason that both patients died within a month after commencing treatment, and before sufficient cumulative effects had been produced to warrant conclusions as to the value of the new therapeutic agent. Mrs. Lee died of systemic carcinosis. Mr. Carr fell on the street, sustaining a fracture of the skull which ultimately caused his death.

Perhaps you ask why I did not, myself, make a written report of these treatments. The answer is: Even though I did this, now considered important, work, I could not, at the time, demand the credit which I felt was due me for two reasons: First, I was not a graduate physician; second, I did not have access to the medical journals. I therefore fancied that I was not in a technical position to obtain credit.

In this connection I contend that merely because my work was not written up in newspapers or medical journals, that fact alone should not exclude me from eligibility for credit. All things that have ever happened in the universe are not necessarily recorded in print. And so, I believe, the recording of an event in a book should not constitute the sole test of validity.

These early treatments with the x-ray were given in a factory—obviously not a good place to serve sick persons. By the end of February, 1896, I had decided to open a properly equipped laboratory for the diagnostic and therapeutic use of x-rays and electric currents. Accordingly, on April 1, 1896, I opened such a laboratory at 2614 Cottage Grove Avenue in Chicago, where I remained for several years.

Now, in order to place the dates of my work in juxtaposition with the historical facts about others for whom claims to priority in x-ray therapeutics have been made, I offer the following:

On January 29, 1896, Dr. T. G. Lyon, of London, wrote a letter to "The Lancet" in which he asked the question: "Do x-rays possess germicidal power?"

On February 4, 1896, there appeared in "Münchener medicinishe Wochenschrift," an article by Dr. F. Mink, pertaining to the exposure of bacteria in culture media to x-rays, with negative results.

In September, 1896, Dr. W. J. Morton, of New York, published a book on x-rays, in which he asserted that he had, during February of that year, i.e., 1896, exposed various bacteria in culture media to x-rays. He found no bactericidal quality in the x-ray.

On February 10, 1896, Thomas Edison stated in the newspapers:

"Now, if they (x-rays) can decompose certain chemicals after they have passed through solid substances, why may they not have the same effect upon the bacilli and bacteria in the body? I somehow feel that the roentgen rays will reach hydrophobia cases and perhaps effect marvelous cures . . . then, again, look at the cases of consumption. Why may not these rays bombard the death-dealing bacilli in the lungs and give them an electro-static quietus?"

On April 10, 1896, in an article which appeared in "Science," Prof. J. Daniel, of Vanderbilt University, wrote that he had exposed the head of Dr. W. C. Dudley for the purpose of making a radiographic test, following which the latter's hair fell out from the side of the head which had been nearest the tube.

In a paper which was read before the Roentgen Society of England, on January 11, 1898, William Webster stated that he first noted therapeutic qualities in the x-ray when, during the latter part of April, 1896, he exposed the elbow joint of a patient repeatedly for the purpose of diagnosis, and found that rheumatic pains, which constituted the principal symptom in the case, were relieved.

In some books dealing with x-rays, Dr. L. Freund, of Vienna, is given credit for being the first to make therapeutic use of these rays. To controvert this claim I need only state that it was not until the Fall of 1896 that Dr. Freund observed the loss of hair in a patient who had been repeatedly exposed to x-rays, and who consulted him for x-ray dermatitis. From that time on, Dr. Freund used x-rays to remove superfluous hair; before that he knew nothing of the therapeutic qualities of these rays.

I have before me a copy of a paper which was read before the Roentgen Society of the United States on September 11, 1901, by Dr. H. P. Pratt, of Chicago, in which he stated the following:

I will now give a brief review of my own work in this field. On the morning of the seventh of February, 1896, I saw the first account of Prof. Roentgen's work. . . . In the first part of April, 1896, with the kind assistance of Prof. Hugo Wightman, I succeeded in destroying the bacilli of eight different diseases, in culture tubes. . . . Immediately after destroying the above cultures, thereby demonstrating the therapeutic value of the ray, I commenced to use it as a therapeutic agent, and on April 13, 1896, . . . I placed my first cancer patient under treatment.

I have quoted Dr. Pratt's paper at length in order to show that at the time when I was actually using x-rays in the treatment of cancer and lupus, *i.e.*, January 28–29, 1896, he (Dr. Pratt) had not yet heard of Roentgen's discovery of x-rays. I wish to point out also that Dr. Pratt states in this paper that he did not give his first x-ray treatment until April 13, 1896. In other words, Dr. Pratt did not actually make use of x-rays in a therapeutic way until *more than ten weeks after* I had made such applications.

Now, if time is the essence in this controversy, then I call on the calendar to place the credit where it belongs. I have gone into the highways and byways looking for information on this point, but I have found nothing which antedates my work in this field. And so, in view of all the foregoing, it would appear that in the therapeutic use of x-rays my work of January 28, 1896, preceded that of all others. Therefore, I feel that I have more than a just claim to whatever honor may be attached to this particular phase of x-ray pioneering.

In conclusion, I also think I am justified in giving Dr. J. E. Gilman, of Chicago, credit for being the first to suggest that x-rays be used in a therapeutic way.

Summing up the evidence which I have submitted, I claim that it allows me to ask credit for being: (1) the first human being exposed to x-rays sufficiently to develop x-ray dermatitis; (2) the first person to apply x-rays to pathologic lesions on living human subjects for therapeutic purposes; (3) the first to use sheet lead, or any other substance, as a protective against untoward x-ray effects.

Appendix 2

In Memoriam

The last survivor of his group of pioneers in the science of radiology, Doctor Emil H. Grubbe died on March 26, 1960. His desire to contribute all his energies toward the advancement of the science of medicine through radiology remained to the end of his life and thus he declined interesting conversation unless it concerned correction of human disabilities, particularly cancer. This was only natural, since he claimed priority as the first to show tissue damage from roentgen rays.

Born in Chicago early on New Year's Day, 1875, of Swiss German stock, Doctor Grubbe was said to be a precocious child. Fortunately he had abundant home support for higher education, for travel, and for research. He was educated in the Chicago public schools and the University of Valparaiso, Indiana, and had private instruction in chemistry, physics, and electricity in this country and in Europe. Having discovered platinum in paying quantities in Idaho, he mined it profitably and was exploring new fields for its use, by introducing it into the manufacture of Crookes tubes, when the threshold of skin tissue tolerance was exceeded on his left hand. This malady added another to the already towering roster of human disabilities, a new entity, radioepidermitis, with its subsequent degenerative effects, caused by the recently discovered X-light of Roentgen.

Before he had reached the age of twenty, Dr. Grubbe had established a laboratory on Pacific Avenue, now LaSalle Street, Chicago. As an assayer of rare metals he early gained a reputation for accuracy and honesty, lifetime characteristics, bringing him a clientele from the large financial institutions engaged in promoting the mining industry of that day. While manufacturing Crookes tubes and in the quest of x-rays, their production and uses, his investigative mind led him to experiment with fluorescing crystals in the crude hat-box type of fluroscope. In the course of these studies he exposed the skin of his face and neck to radiation beyond the point of tolerance. He also suffered excessive total-body irradiation, narrowly escaping death from blood dyscrasias, and incurred other disabilities, including sterility. His life was saved at this time, he believed, by consulting Sir William Osler, who suggested the newly developed medication of fresh ox blood and liver. While his sterility was as yet not realized, it later became a major factor in his unhappy marital relations and the loneliness of his childless life.

Reprinted from *Radiology*, LXXV, No. 3 (September, 1900), 473–74.

Emil H. Grubbe

The first x-ray apparatus in a Chicago hospital was designed, assembled, and operated by Doctor Grubbe in 1896 (the Hahnemann Hospital of Chicago). Among his other hospital connections of earlier years, Chicago Memorial, Baptist, Frances E. Willard, Streeter Memorial Hospital, and the Pine and Peekskill Sanitariums may be cited. His laboratory in Hahnemann Hospital became the nucleus of the first department for teaching radiology to students in a medical school (the Hahnemann Hospital and Medical College).

When the faculty of the Illinois College of Electrotherapeutics decided to include "and x-rays," Dr. Grubbe was given the responsibility of teaching this new division. In this period of expanding usefulness of x-rays, the shift of emphasis from electrotherapeutics toward radiology created opposing groups in medical practice, and x-ray and Roentgen societies were organized with only minor stress on electrotherapeutics. It was also a time in medical history when fiery tempers clashed, of bitter frustration, vigorous determinations, rigorous oppositions, and of hard fought victories from which there emerged entirely new concepts of pre- and postgraduate medical education, organization, and practice which created a real revolution in medical affairs.

This situation, coupled with mounting disabilities resulting from successive episodes of surgical amputations and tumor removals, marked a crucial point in Dr. Grubbe's professional career. Obviously his efforts to include x-rays in the old societies failed when the Chicago Roentgen Society, and the national radiological organizations were formed by different groups of physicians. He remained, however, a staunch supporter of organized medical bodies throughout his life and was a founding member of the Roentgen Society of the United States, later the American Roentgen Ray Society. He had been a member of the Radiological Society of North America since 1915.

Honorary awards were conferred by the American Institute of Medicine, the Walter Reed Society, the Chicago Roentgen Society, the American Cancer Society, and the Chicago Medical Society. Doctor Grubbe was a member of the Citizens Board of the University of Chicago, the American Congress of Physical Therapy (1938), the Association of American Physicians and Surgeons, the National Academy of Science, the American Association for Cancer Research, the National Society for Physical Therapeutics (President, 1912), the Illinois State and the Chicago Medical Societies, the Chicago Roentgen Society, the American Society for the Advancement of Science, the American Philosophical Society, the Chicago Philatelic Society (President, 1939), and the American Philatelic Society. He was a delegate to the International Electric Congress in 1904 and a Fellow of the American College of Physicians and the American Medical Association.

In the provisions of his will Doctor Grubbe established "The Emil H. Grubbe Radiation Therapy Foundation of the University of Chicago." Some ten years earlier he had made a gift to the John Crerar Library, Chicago, of his private library consisting of about a thousand volumes on roentgenography, roentgen therapy, and related technical subjects.

To appreciate the full significance of Doctor Grubbe's accomplishments, one must understand that he was ambitious, blessed with a storehouse of energy, strong physical endurance, a brilliant mind, all channeled into the single purpose of alleviating human suffering through medical science. With courage and fortitude he gave his all.

BENJAMIN H. ORNDOFF, M.D.